MW00777993

CASTING
ALUMINUM

C.W. AMMEN

TAB BOOKS Inc.

Blue Ridge Summit, PA 17214

Notices:

Petro-Bond is a registered trademark of NL Industries, Baroid Division.
Selee is a registered trademark of Consolidated Aluminum Corporation.
Tenzaloy is a trademark of Federated Metals.

This book is dedicated to my wife, Hazel, and my son, Charles Andrew Ammen.

FIRST EDITION

FIRST PRINTING

Printed in the United States of America

Library of Congress Cataloging in Publication Date

Ammen, C. W.
    Casting aluminum.

    Includes index.
    1. Aluminum founding. I. Title.
TS555.A766   1985   673'.7222   84-26744
ISBN 0-8306-0910-5
ISBN 0-8306-1910-0 (pbk.)

Contents

Introduction

Why a book on casting aluminum? There is much in common with all metals as far as general foundry practice goes. You have sand, flasks, patterns, melting, cores, etc., regardless of the type of metal you intend to cast. A *casting* is a metal object produced by pouring liquid metal into a mold cavity. When the metal solidifies in the mold, it assumes the shape of the mold cavity. The mold is removed, leaving a casting of the desired shape. This is true for steel, brass, iron, aluminum, etc. Each different metal, however, requires a different set of foundry conditions and practices dictated by the properties and characteristics of the particular metal: melting temperature, specific gravity, chemical structure, solidification range, etc. You have to melt any metal to cast it; however, a device to melt and superheat an aluminum alloy is not suitable for steel or gray iron.

This book covers the foundry practices necessary to produce aluminum castings. General foundry practices for sand casting are covered in the *Complete Handbook of Sand Casting* (TAB Book No. 1043). In this book I cover differences in foundry practice that are peculiar to aluminum as I have done for iron in *Casting Iron* (TAB Book No. 1610).

Of all the metals suitable to a small foundry operation or a hobby, cast aluminum is probably the simplest, easiest, and cheapest to get into and can be done profitably on a very small scale. You don't see any small backyard steel foundries, simply because of the differences in practice that I have just discussed. There is a big difference in melting and superheating steel to 32,000 degrees Fahrenheit in an arc furnace and melting and superheating aluminum alloys to 1450 degrees Fahrenheit in a simple, homemade, charcoal garbage-can furnace.

There has been an ever-growing interest in aluminum in all forms—forging, extrusions, weldments, and especially castings. With the ease that aluminum alloys can be melted and cast with a minimum amount of equipment and material invested, along with the fact that aluminum alloys can be readily cast by any number of methods available and the ever-increasing available types of alloys, the caster has a wide selection of desirable properties, such as tensile strength, elongation, machinability, welding ability, casting ability, and yield strength.

There are countless aluminum alloys that have special properties. Some are heat-treatable; some are self-aging, high-strength alloys that, for example, have an as-cast tensile strength of 29,000 PSI, and after simply setting around the shop for 10 to 16 hours at room temperature, the sand-cast tensile strength jumps to 35,000 PSI. The same alloy cast in a permanent mold would have a tensile strength as cast of 30,000 PSI; after 16 hours at room temperature, the tensile strength would jump to 40,000 PSI. Some of these special alloys actually show better properties by self-aging at room temperature than you would accomplish by artificial aging, with the added bonus that the equipment and cost of heat treating is eliminated. Aluminum can be sand-cast in green sand molds, dry sand molds, core molds, no-bake molds, loam, permanent cast-iron or carbon molds, diecast, centrifugal cast, continuous cast, simple plaster molds, squeeze cast, frozen mold process (Effset), magnetic molds, EPS molds (expanded polystyrene molding), cement bonded molds, composition molds, Petro-Bonded molds, or skin-dry molds.

Aluminum and its alloys can be easily melted in a large variety of furnace equipment: open-flame rotaries, open-flame (wet or dry) hearth reverberatories, coke fired, gas fired, electric glow rod rigs, induction rigs, chromalloy radiant heated rigs, blacksmith's forge, cast-iron frying pan or plumber's cast-iron lead pot in the forge, a tree-hung stove pipe melter, a charcoal-fired garbage-can melter with a hair dryer, even a hand bellows or a bicycle-driven blower. It can be melted in cast-iron pots, welded steel pots, regular crucibles, or on the open hearth. The molding medium (green sand, dry sand, etc.) need not be very refractory or open-grained or require near as much green and/or dry strength as you would require for cast iron or brass. Sands can be very fine, even for large castings, and will give you a fine-finish, easy-clean peel because of the relatively low pouring temperature.

The sand has a much longer life and requires less attention. The castings can be polished to a high polish, are light in weight, and will take all sorts of surface treatment and coloring such as anodizing. Casting defects are limited and easy to solve. Aluminum and its alloys are extremely fluid at pouring temperatures, so very thin castings can be poured.

The foundry practice is simpler from every angle and cost; so aluminum is an ideal metal, especially for the fledgling caster. You could comprise a list of items produced a mile and a half long, as well as a few thousand more items, formerly cast in brass, steel, or cast iron, that are now cast in aluminum. Many of these items are now aluminum and painted black. Many new items cast in aluminum would have been cast in gray iron 20 to 25 years ago.

Even items which would be better suited in cast iron are found cast in aluminum today. There was a time when pig iron was very cheap, labor was cheap, coke was cheap, and you could throw together a cupola and run it. Now with a million dollars of baghouse, fume scrubbers, dust arresters, etc., all this has changed.

For the hobby caster or the person with only a little product, if he can go with aluminum castings in a small operation in a back building with no noise and little smoke, his neighbors would never know. A small melter, a pile of natural bonded river sand, a few wooden flasks, a rammer, a riddle or two, a molding shovel, and a few odds and ends are all you need. If you simply look around and take notice, you will find aluminum castings everywhere, from machine parts, builders' hardware, cooking utensils, patterns and core boxes, prototype work, marine hardware, automotive parts and trim, art work, tool parts, valves, gears, levers, cranks, plaques, pumps, blowers, aircraft parts, ash trays, novelties, and various hardware, including file handles, to hinges, electrical hardware, motor bells, and frames. I worked on the castings for the continental tank engine—a V12 air-cooled engine that was by and large a huge assembly of aluminum castings.

I know of several cases where small, so-called backyard manufacturers, whose product is one or more aluminum castings, have set up a small side operation to produce their own castings to reduce their cost per unit and increase their profit. One I know of will spend several months making up a supply of his needed aluminum castings, then shut down his little foundry and move over to his machine shop for a few months. Nothing is more versatile than a casting or a cast product. To change products, you simply change pattern equipment—that is, sand cast products.

Often, even though the intended product is going to be produced in a material other than aluminum, the prototype, its parts, etc., are first cast in aluminum. It is the cheapest, simplest, quickest, and easiest method to come up with something solid from a blueprint, notes, or simple vision. Once you have this, final development is easily worked out. It was quite common for the pattern shop in a foundry to have a small aluminum sand casting set-up to test or prove various designs and concepts prior to nailing down the design and producing expensive production patterns or tooling.

1

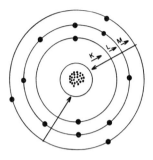

Aluminum

Although this volume is basically concerned with the casting of aluminum and its alloys, various aspects of the foundry practice, and the problems involved in the production of high-grade aluminum castings at a minimum of cost and effort, you should consider just exactly what aluminum is and how it is recovered from its ore bauxite.

Although your primary interest might be in getting from the aluminum to the casting, the more you understand about aluminum and its alloys, the better off you will be. *Aluminum* is the metallic element abbreviated Al. The atomic number is 13, and it is in Group IIIA of the Periodic Table of the Elements. The atomic weight is 26.9815 and the valence is $+3$.

CHEMISTRY OF ALUMINUM

Figure 1-1 shows the simple schematic shell structure of an aluminum atom. The nucleus of the aluminum atom contains 13 positive particles, or *protons*, and 14 neutral particles, or *neutrons*, around which orbit 13 negative particles, or *electrons*, in 3 orbits: K, L, and M. In the K orbit are two electrons, in the L orbit are 8 electrons, and in the M orbit are 3 electrons. The 13 positive charges and 13 negative charges cancel out each other. This atomic arrangement gives aluminum its properties, making it different from other elements, such as shown in Fig. 1-2.

In iron there are 26 positive particles in the nucleus, balanced out with 2 negative in the K orbit, 8 negative in the L orbit, 14 negative in the M orbit, and 2 in the N orbit. Aluminum and iron are made of the same thing—positive and negative particles, called *energy bundles*. Although they are made of the same thing, however, the number and atomic arrangement is different, making them two different materials.

Now, let's look at the word *valence*. I said that the valence of aluminum was a plus 3. What I am talking about is the three electrons in the M orbit. Aluminum is an atom with an incompletely filled outer orbit or *shell*. Any atom with less than eight electrons tends to react with other atoms, so it ends up with a completed outer orbit of eight electrons. Aluminum has three electrons that it can donate to another atom which has a negative valence to form a compound. The number of electrons an atom will gain or lose in a chemical reaction is the valence. In trying to fill its outer shell with eight electrons, it will take the shortest route. If it has three electrons in its outer orbit and five empty spaces, it would like to lose the three outer electrons, not try to pick up five from somewhere else. If an atom has seven electrons in its outer shell, it only lacks one to be complete. It will not give up its seven in a reaction, but it will remove an electron from another atom to fill its shell. An atom of this structure would have a negative valence of 1, whereas our aluminum has a positive 3 valence.

Most elements with one, two, or three electrons in their outer shell are metals and have a positive valence of one, two, or three. Those that are minus one, two, or three electrons in their outer orbit are nonmetals.

Fluorine has a nucleus of nine protons, two electrons in the K orbit, and seven electrons in the L orbit, giving it a valence of −1. Oxygen has a nucleus of eight protons with two electrons in the K orbit and six electrons in the L orbit for a valence of −2. Nitrogen has a nucleus of seven protons, with two electrons in the K orbit and five electrons in the L orbit, and a valence of −3.

Carbon is an exception to the rule. It has four electrons in its outer shell (Fig. 1-3). Is the valence +4 or −4? Atoms which have four electrons in their outer shell are neither metals nor nonmetals and usually neither lose nor gain electrons when they react. They include silicon and germanium.

Let's look again at the aluminum atom. This atomic solar system has a central "sun"—the nucleus consisting of 13 protons and 14 neutrons. Around this sun circles 13 worlds—electrons. These worlds are grouped in definite orbital zones. The outer or-

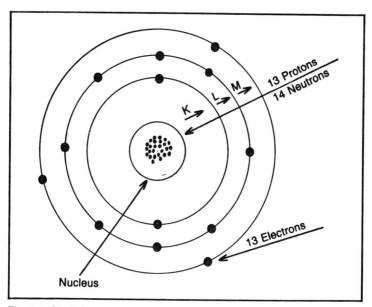

Fig. 1-1. Shell diagram of an aluminum atom.

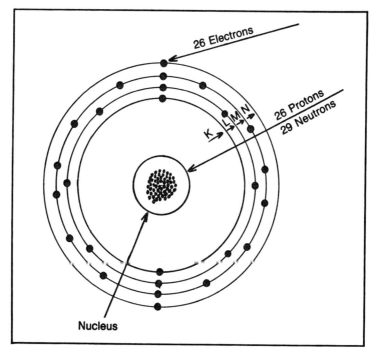

Fig. 1-2. Shell diagram of an iron atom.

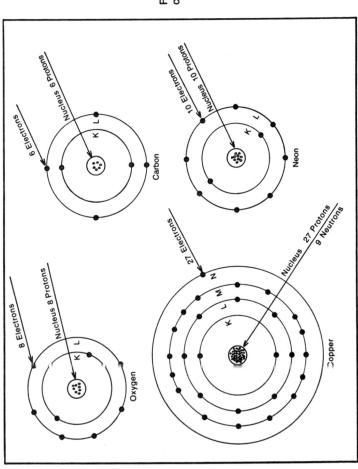

Fig. 1-3. Ring structure of oxygen, carbon, copper, and neon atoms.

bit contains 3 lonely worlds.

Because these three are relatively distant from the sun, they are held less strongly by the positive attraction forces of the positive sun. They are easily picked off to combine with atoms of other elements to form compounds.

Let's look at the oxygen atom (Fig. 1-4). Here you have an atom which needs only two electrons for its completion. So, if oxygen atoms and aluminum atoms come together under the right conditions, you wind up with a new compound—aluminum oxide (Al_2O_3). Two atoms of aluminum, which have between them six electrons to donate, will couple up with three oxygen atoms, which require six electrons to complete the outer shell.

Because the aluminum atom tends to easily lose its outer three electrons, as do most metals, and because all matter is constantly seeking to attain a neutral charge, these electrons are given to some source, many cases a nonmetal. As oxygen is readily available and

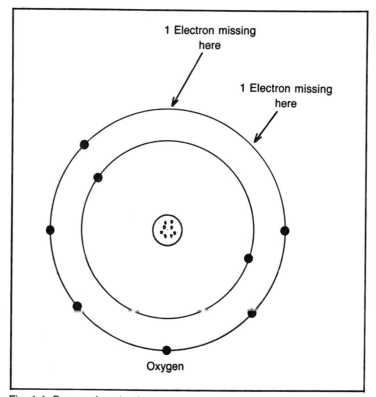

Fig. 1-4. Oxygen ring structure.

will form a very stable compound with aluminum very easily, pure aluminum is never found in a free state in nature, but only as a part of a compound, usually an oxide. As this aluminum oxide is so stable, the bond between the oxygen and the aluminum is extremely difficult to break, so much so that you have probably never seen pure aluminum.

Alloys

The instant pure aluminum is exposed to the atmosphere, the oxygen instantly hooks up with the aluminum atoms on its surface to form a coat of aluminum oxide over the entire surface. This surface coating of aluminum oxide (Al_2O_3) isolates the aluminum below it from further attack by oxygen. Of course, once this coat is removed, a new coat instantly forms. By this action you could remove the oxide, let it form up again, remove it, and so on until it's all back to oxide.

If left alone, this outer layer of oxide is adherent and impervious; hence aluminum is a self-protective metal. This layer of aluminum oxide is what gives aluminum a slightly bluish tint. Because the color of the oxide resembles that of the metal so much, most people are likely to think that aluminum does not tarnish at all. This aluminum oxide coating can be colored various decorative hues by a system called *anodizing.*

This affinity for aluminum to combine with oxygen is one of the problems with pouring a sound casting. You must watch out that aluminum does not combine with oxygen from the products of combustion when melting or from its contact with oxygen during pouring or pouring through an improperly designed gating system, or, for the matter, with the oxygen in the mold cavity.

Aluminum also has an affinity for hydrogen, which leads to problems of gas porosity in the solidified castings unless the metal is properly degassed prior to pouring. The fact that aluminum will couple easily with various other elements is an advantage, because it gives us a host of very valuable and useful compounds. The fact that aluminum will combine so easily with oxygen makes it possible to produce oxygen-free steel

Some very valuable aluminum compounds include aluminum acetate ($Al(C_2H_3O_2)_3$), used for waterproofing, mordant, dyeing, embalming fluids, treatment of dermatitis, and calico printing; aluminum acetylsalicylate $[C6H_4 (OCOCH_3) (COO)]_2 AlOH,$) used in medicine; aluminum alloys for casting, forging, drawing, rolling, welding, etc., over a wide range of strength, corrosion resistance, machinability, weldability, etc.; aluminum ammonium chloride ($AlCl_3 \cdot NH_4Cl$) used for fur treatment; aluminum boride, for nuclear shielding; and aluminum borohydride ($Al(BH_4)_3$), a jet fuel additive.

Aluminum Ore

As I stated, aluminum is never found free in nature but is combined with oxygen. This principal ore is called bauxite ($Al_2O_3 \cdot 2H_2O$) or alumina.

Bauxite is a noncrystalline earthy white to reddish mineral found as a massive material or in grains. The highest-grade bauxite (aluminum ore) contains 74 percent alumina. The next grade down would be called high-grade bauxite Grade A, which contains 55 percent alumina. Grade B is 50 percent alumina. Chemical grades of alumina contain up to 84 percent alumina with a maximum of 2.5 percent iron oxide. Only bauxite that has an alumina content of 45 percent or more is considered practical for the production of aluminum metal (reduction). If the bauxite ore is of too low a grade of alumina, it is simply not commercially feasible.

Let's look at a typical commercial grade of bauxite—45 to 60 percent alumina, 3 to 25 percent iron oxide, 2.5 to 18 percent silicon oxide, 2 to 5 percent titanium oxide, and up to 1 percent other impurities. Couple this with 12 to 30 percent water of crystallization, and you get $.2H_2O$ behind the formula $Al_2O_3 \cdot 2H_2O$, which can vary.

Water of Crystallization is simply water which is chemically combined with certain substances in the crystalline state. When I state $Al_2O_3 \cdot 2H_2O$, for every molecule of Al_2O_3, there are two molecules of water chemically combined with the Al_2O_3 (as opposed to free water).

Taking this ore as an average, one long ton (2,240 pounds) will yield 0.87 long ton (1948.8 pounds of dried bauxite. To produce 2000 pounds (1 short ton) of aluminum, it takes 4,000 pounds of alumina. So, you can see that the process of going from raw bauxite to bauxite that is ready to produce aluminum is not a backyard operation. It takes on the average of 1.2 pounds of soda ash to flux out each pound of silica in the raw bauxite alone.

The next move from clean bauxite to metallic aluminum is the real kicker. More on this later.

Let's look at the alumina and some of its uses other than the production of metallic aluminum. The list is quite long, so I will only list a few. Many industries other than aluminum producers depend upon alumina as their main raw material for their product. Here are a few uses of alumina: manufacture of abrasives, refractories, ceramics, electrical insulators, catalysts, catalyst supports, paper making, spark plugs, crucibles, chemical lab ware, absorbing gasses and water vapor, chromatographic analysis, fluxes, light bulbs, artificial gems, heat-resistant fibers, and hundreds of various chemical compounds which are used in all fields of endeavor from medicine to tanning leather, water purification, etc. We have enough know bauxite deposits to last for many thousands of years, and new deposits are still being found. Most, but not all of the raw bauxite deposits are relatively shallow so they are easy and cheap to strip mine. There is little likelihood that we will run out of raw stock.

SOME ALUMINUM HISTORY

The compound of aluminum and oxygen is called bauxite, after Les Baux, France, where it was first discovered in 1821.

The Puzzle

In order to break the extraordinary chemical and physical bond which holds aluminum and oxygen together, we must roll back the clock billions of years and reverse the process which formed the aluminum oxide. For many centuries, men tried to unlock this mystery. The material was called *the Metal of Clay* and was used widely by potters for the production of special pottery that was strong and very refractory.

As far back as 5300 B.C., the clay, which consisted of hydrated silicate of aluminum, was used to make fine pottery. The potters found that the use of this aluminous clay produced pots which not only could be used to carry water, etc., but were refractory enough to be used for cooking.

Other aluminum compounds contain sulfates and are called *alums*. Aluminum sulfate is the trade name for alum, pearl alum, pickled alum, cake alum, filter alum, paper maker's alum, and patent alum. These alums were widely used by the Egyptians and Babylonians as far back as 2000 B.C. for such things as medicine, various chemical processes, dyes, and cosmetics.

Despite the fact that man has used bauxite in one way or another for 7000 years, no one was yet successful in breaking the bond between the aluminum and the oxygen. It is no doubt that it was recognized or at least presumed by some to be an oxide of metal because of the way it acted and could be used.

Redox

Most metal ores are in the form of a compound. Let's take the simple case of iron ore, which is magnetite (Fe_3O_4) and is an oxide of iron. It is actually a simple matter to come up with metallic iron. All you have to do is get the oxygen interested in combining with something else, leaving the iron. The most-used process is the blast furnace. The oxygen combines with the fuel (coke) to form carbon monoxide then carbon dioxide. The oxygen in the magnetite enters into the combustion process in the blast furnace, supplying oxygen to oxidize the coke—a simple reduction with carbon. The iron is left in the bottom of the furnace in the form of gray iron, iron and combined carbon, and free graphitic carbon. From there, if you free the carbon from the iron, you have pure iron. If you leave some carbon in the iron as chemically combined carbon, you have steel. This is the other side of the redox.

$$\text{Oxidation} \rightleftharpoons \text{Reduction}$$
$$\text{Rust} \rightleftharpoons \text{Iron}$$

This process is easily reversed; so we can go back to iron oxide.

Let's look at alumina, which is nothing more than aluminum rust (Al_2O_3). Why can't we drive the oxygen out, or do the reduction side of the redox simply? Most other known metals can be reduced or separated from their compounds by some simple method. It could be chemically separated, beaten out under the hammer, or driven out by fire. Why should aluminum's affinity for oxygen be so strong that it cannot be overcome by carbon or any other known reducing agents? It sure doesn't look tough. In fact it looks simpler than magnetite. So this was the puzzle.

It was not until the middle of the 18th century that some of the investigators began to believe that alum contained two bases and not just terra calcaria, a limelike substance with which alum had been identified since 1702.

Lavoisier

Antoine L. Lavoisier was born in 1743. This great French

chemist was the first to popularize quantitive methods in chemistry, and he did extensive work on the nature of combustion. Lavoisier said, "It is highly probable that alumina is an oxide of a metal whose affinity for oxygen is so strong that it cannot be overcome either by carbon or any other known reducing agent." Had he lived, he could have been the father of aluminum.

He served in the revolution, was tried on flimsy charges during the Reign of Terror, and was executed on May 8, 1794. The leaders of the reign of terror said there was no need for men of science. Although his life span was short (51 years), he contributed much to the understanding of chemistry. He wrote the first modern chemical textbook, *Traite Elementaire de Chimie*, in 1789, which soon found its way through Europe.

Davy

Sir Humphry Davy was born in 1778 and died in 1829. He took up the aluminum puzzle. In 1807 he had been successful in reducing metallic potassium and metallic sodium by the electrolysis of potash and soda. He was also able to isolate calcium, barium, boron, magnesium, and strontium by his ingenious electrical disassociation processes. Assuming that he was on the right track, he tackled alumina. He was convinced, like Lavoisier, that alumina was indeed an oxide with a metallic base. He gave this hypothetical elusive metal the name aluminum, from the Roman *alumine*. He felt it sounded more scientific than the old name of Metal of Clay. Today in the United States it is still spelled aluminum as Davy spelled it; however, elsewhere it's spelled aluminium. Although Davy was unsuccessful in coming up with a true reduction process for aluminum, he did succeed in producing an iron-aluminum alloy by fusing a mixture of alumina and iron in an electric arc furnace. You could say that, for a microsecond before the aluminum combined with the iron, there was in existence free aluminum, probably the first time since the world was formed.

Davy is remembered mainly for his work with electrochemistry; however, as the inventor of the miner's safety lamp, he is responsible for saving the lives of countless men who work underground. The miner's safety lamp was an offshoot of his work with combustion. Davy has the title, "the Father of Electrochemistry." He postulated the theory that chemical affinity is an electrical phenomenon.

Oersted

Hans Christian Oersted was born in 1777 and died in 1851. He was a Danish physicist. The centimeter-gram-second electromagnetic unit of magnetic intensity is called an Oersted (Oe) after him.

Oersted was the first man to actually come up with a process for making aluminum, or whereby it can be released from the grip of oxygen. After all you don't make aluminum; it is simply hidden away as a component of alumina.

In 1825, he told the Royal Danish Academy of Sciences in Copenhagen that he had found the metal in the metal of clay. He produced some aluminum by heating potassium amalgam with aluminum chloride and found aluminum embedded in the amalgam.

This was the first time man had a process for making metallic aluminum. Oersted described the aluminum he produced as a lump of metal which in color and luster somewhat resembled tin.

Wohler

Friedrich Wohler (born 1800, died 1882) tried to reduce alumina to aluminum via Oersted's experiment but failed. In 1845, while he was working at the University of Gottingen, he succeeded in making some aluminum particles as big as pinheads. He said aluminum is a light, ductile metal stable in the air and easily melted under a blow pipe (Fig. 1-5).

Sainte-Claire Deville

Deville really solved the puzzle in 1855. He produced aluminum in a pure state, by the reaction of sodium with a double chloride

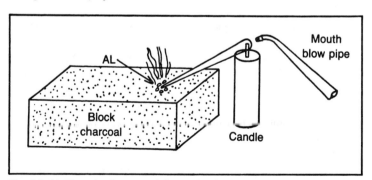

Fig. 1-5. Melting aluminum particles under the blow pipe.

of aluminum and sodium. Deville refused all credit for the reduction of aluminum and insisted Wohler was the real genius.

Deville's success was the talk of the Paris Exposition of 1867, where he exhibited an aluminum ingot which weighed several pounds. Deville also achieved the decomposition of water vapor, gaseous hydrogen chloride, and carbon dioxide gas.

What he did with aluminum was to substitute sodium for potassium, which produced aluminum in lumps the size of marbles in place of Wohler's pinhead-sized particles. In 1855 commercial plants using Deville's process were producing aluminum. Prior to 1852, aluminum was priceless. In 1852 it was available at $545 per pound. By 1855 it was $155 per pound, but by 1859 it dropped to $17 per pound.

Heroult, Hall, and Bayer

Paul L.T. Heroult, working in Paris, and Charles Martin Hall, working in Ohio, came up with a workable electrolytic process at almost precisely the same time—February 23, 1886. This is an odd coincidence, even more so because both men were born in 1863 and both died in 1914.

Karl Joseph Bayer invented a process for making pure aluminum oxide from low-silica-content bauxite ores, and a process for preparing iron-pure alumina hydrate from bauxite.

What Heroult, Hall, and Bayer accomplished together was to free aluminum from the oxygen, making it easy to produce on a huge scale as the world's most plentiful and useful structural element.

PRODUCTION OF ALUMINUM

Let's look at what goes into the production of one pound of aluminum. The recipe is raw bauxite—4 pounds; coal—1/2 pound; fuel oil—1/4 pound; soda—1/2 pound; and lime—1/8 pound. Process this in your alumina plant, and you come up with 2 pounds of pure alumina.

Combine the 2 pounds of alumina with .030 pounds of cryolite (Na_3AlF_6), which is the flux. It is a very powerful flux because of its solvent power on silicon, aluminum, and calcium oxides.

Next add 1/25 pound of aluminum fluoride (AlF_3). Now you have a mixture of alumina, cryolite, and aluminum fluoride. Add to this 8 kilowatt hours of electricity, and you come up with 1 pound of aluminum.

Chemical Reduction

Now let's look at the process of the reduction of aluminum from raw bauxite. The raw bauxite contained in the aluminum ore consists of 40 to 60 percent aluminum oxide, 3 to 25 percent iron oxide, 2.5 to 18 percent silicon oxide, 12 to 30 percent water of crystallization, and up to 1 percent various other impurities. This would approximate a good ore; however, there can be various differences in percents and content, depending on where the ore body is found.

If you are prospecting for bauxite, its specific gravity is 2.70, and it is a noncrystalline earthy white to reddish mineral, massive or in grains. It looks like clay, but when rubbed between the fingers, it is reduced to a fine powder. Clay will not do this. Dry a small sample of what you suspect is bauxite and grind it up in a small mortar. If it is bauxite, it will stick like glue to the sides and bottom of your mortar; dry clay will not.

Bauxite will not scratch glass; clay will. It is not gritty between the teeth; clay is. It will not fuse under the blow pipe. A pinch with a drop or two of cobalt nitrate solution placed on a charcoal block and heated strongly under a blow pipe will turn blue if it is bauxite.

The raw bauxite must be dried and ground. It is then mixed with a strong solution of caustic soda (sodium hydroxide). The alumina is soluble in this strong base solution and forms sodium aluminate ($Na_2Al_2O_3$). The silica present in the raw bauxite reacts and precipitates out; the remaining impurities simply settle out.

You are left with a *green liquor* of supersaturated sodium aluminate. The solution, minus the solids that settled or precipitated out, is placed in huge towers, called *precipitor towers*, some as tall as a five-story building. The green liquor is then seeded with previously prepared hydrated alumina crystals. When added to the liquor, it starts a chain reaction—these seeds attract other crystals and form groups that become heavy enough to settle out of the solution. The product is concentrated alumina hydrate crystals. The stripped liquor which is partially spent is kept to be used in the next batch of dried and ground bauxite ore.

The resulting alumina hydrate, which is also called hydrated alumina, alumina trihydrate, alumina hydroxide, or hydrated aluminum oxide, is then washed to remove any remaining impurities. The next step is to remove the water of crystallization by roasting the aluminum hydrate crystals at temperatures in excess of 2000 degrees Fahrenheit.

If each step was carried out properly, the result is a fine, white, sugarlike powder that is about half aluminum and half oxygen. The aluminum and oxygen are chemically bonded so tightly that the bond cannot be broken by chemicals or heat alone. Note: The decrystallization of the hydrated alumina crystals by seeding the green liquor can be accomplished via neutralization of the liquor with carbon dioxide.

Up to now all that has been accomplished is to remove the alumina from the gangue of the bauxite and to remove the water of crystallization, leaving a pure, anhydrous alumina.

Alumina hydrate ($Al_2O_3.3H_2O$ or $Al(OH)_3$) plus heat to drive off the water of crystallization equals anhydrous alumina (Al_2O_3). What has been done is simply high-grading the bauxite ore to just alumina via chemical means, often called *ore dressing and concentrating.*

As a native of New Orleans, I watched this operation over the years. The bauxite came up the Mississippi River to Baton Rouge, where it was processed to pure alumina, and then the pure alumina was shipped back down the river to Chalmette, Louisiana, just below New Orleans, where the alumina was reduced to metallic aluminum by electric reduction. In the area where the bauxite was processed in Baton Rouge, every building was covered with red iron oxide from the bauxite. The name Baton Rouge means Red Stick.

Remember Wohler came up with some aluminum in pinhead-sized pieces by heating strongly a mixture of anhydrous aluminum chloride and potassium. He, no doubt, went this route when he was unsuccessful in reducing with carbon.

Hall's Process

Hall's process was simply to mix bauxite reduced to pure high grade alumina with cryolite and aluminum fluoride and place them in a cell lined with carbon (Fig. 1-6).

When dc current is applied to the cell, the cryolite and aluminum fluoride melt, and the aluminum oxide dissolves readily in the fused flux of aluminum fluoride and cryolite. The electric current liberates the aluminum ions of the oxygen. The liberated aluminum, being heavier than the flux, settles to the bottom of the cell, where it is tapped off from time to time and additional alumina added to the cells. It is a continuous process. Some of the oxygen released from the alumina goes off as oxygen bubbles, and some of it combines with the carbon anode to form carbon dioxide. This

14

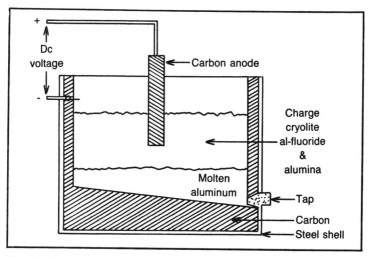

Fig. 1-6. Simple Hall cell.

combination of oxygen with the carbon anode slowly destroys the anode, requiring it to be replaced as needed. Of course, commercial cells are quite large and contain numerous anodes.

The success of this process depends upon cheap electrical power. The cells are called *pots*, and a pot line consists of a series of pots wired together in series. Although they are called pots, they are rectangular. Depending upon the design, the molten metal is either tapped from the side or the end of the pot or siphoned off into large preheated crucibles. The aluminum in each crucible is analyzed for purity and is then ready to be cast, or further alloyed then cast, into ingots, slabs, continuous casting shapes, etc.

The aluminum, as it comes from the pot line, is usually 99.5 percent pure, and from this basic aluminum a huge family of various alloys is produced. Some aluminum is purified to 99.99 percent and is called *superpure*. It is used for foil, cans, electronic industry, catalyst carriers, deoxidizers, etc. The largest tonnage of aluminum is alloyed.

Aluminum Series Grouping

Aluminum is broken down into eight series. Series 1000 consists of commercially pure aluminum (99 percent pure). Series 2000 consists of aluminum alloyed with copper. Series 3000 consists of aluminum alloyed with manganese. Series 4000 consists of aluminum alloyed with silicon. Series 5000 consists of aluminum

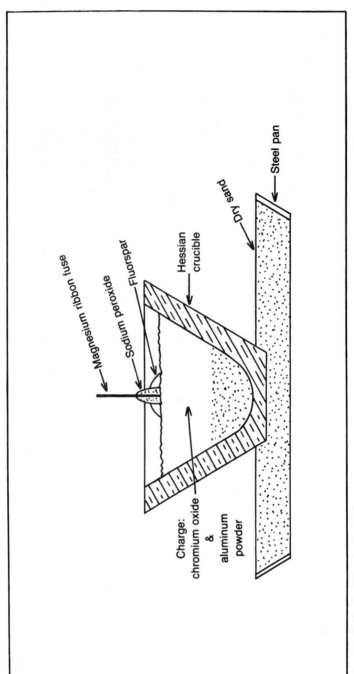

Fig. 1-7. Goldschmidt reduction cell.

alloyed with magnesium. Series 6000 consists of aluminum alloyed with magnesium and silicon. Series 7000 consists of aluminum alloyed with zinc. Series 8000 consists of aluminum alloyed with other alloys.

Diversified Uses of Aluminum

The uses of aluminum are too numerous to list. The disassociation, or reduction, of aluminum from alumina is, as you see, a problem; however the great affinity of aluminum for oxygen is an extremely useful tool and is widely used.

When a mixture of aluminum powder and an oxide of a metal such as copper oxide, iron oxide, or chromium oxide, is ignited by a magnesium ribbon, a chemical reaction begins. The aluminum combines with the oxygen of the particular metal oxide producing aluminum oxide and metal (reduced metal in the molten state).

$$\text{Aluminum} + \text{Iron Oxide} + \text{(The Heat of Reaction)}$$
$$= \text{Aluminum Oxide} + \text{Molten Iron}$$

This thermite reaction produces a great quantity of heat. The reaction is used for welding, incendiary bombs, etc. The *Goldschmidt Process* is a thermite process used to extract certain metals from their oxides.

In Fig. 1-7, when the magnesium ribbon is ignited, it burns down, igniting the small pile of sodium peroxide and aluminum. At this point, the reaction begins with almost explosive violence. The heat produced by the sodium peroxide-aluminum combustion starts the reaction of the chromium oxide and aluminum mixture reaction. When the reaction is complete, and the crucible is cooled, a button of metallic chromium is found at the bottom of the crucible.

17

2

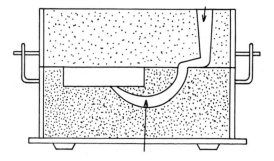

Alloyed Aluminum

You will probably have little cause to actually cast pure aluminum because of its low strength and softness; however, should you need to do so, you will find it acts very similar to pure copper. You get into gating and feeding problems. The volumetric shrinkage for pure aluminum is quite high, requiring very large risers and very high copes to supply hydrostatic pressure to the casting and so assist in feeding heavy sections. Pure aluminum is also much more susceptible to oxidization from the products of combustion of your melting rig.

Every now and then someone will melt down a pile of aluminum beer cans to cast something, only to realize after the fact that this material is very nearly pure aluminum, and the castings present problems. Problems also exist with *binary aluminum alloys,* which are compounds of aluminum with one other element only. These alloys are difficult to cast and are weak in strength.

In order to produce aluminum castings that have the required characteristics, the pure aluminum is alloyed by the refiner with various metallic and nonmetallic elements and combinations of these for the desired ingot specifications. The founder only needs to select from a wide variety of specifications the ingot that will give him exactly what he wishes in the way of a pedigree for his casting. Although aluminum is alloyed with a fairly large family of additions (elements), we are only concerned with the most common—

copper, silicon, and magnesium and, to a lesser extent, iron, manganese, and zinc.

There is a selection of aluminum alloys of special nature designed for special purposes, such as very high strength and toughness. To cite an example, consolidated aluminium has an ingot called A201 with a chemical composition of 4.7 percent copper, 0.5 percent silver, 0.30 percent magnesium, 0.20 percent titanium, and 94.3 percent aluminum. This combination gives you very high tensile strength—60,000 PSI at room temperature with 3.0 percent elongation in 2 inches—and excellent tensile strength up to 500 degrees Fahrenheit, making it a strong, heat-treatable alloy. This alloy is used in a wide variety of air, military, and automotive vehicles—anywhere you would need superior strength coupled with light weight.

Of course, the selection depends on the ultimate end use of the casting. As with all metals, you have such a wide variety of alloys that it can become very confusing. The percentage of alloying elements is usually limited to about 15 percent of the total. Beyond this point, the resulting aluminum alloy becomes brittle and useless. The exception to the rule is with master alloys. These are alloys compounded to alloy a pure aluminum or adjust the heat of scrap aluminum. In other words, should you wish to add copper to a pure aluminum, you could do it with copper clippings, wire, etc. It is much simpler, however, if you purchase a master alloy of 50 percent aluminum and 50 percent copper, and calculate the required amount of hardener against your weight of pure aluminum for the desired percent of copper content. Let's look at the individual effects of various common alloying elements.

COPPER

Copper added to pure aluminum will improve aluminum's strength and hardness; however, above 12 percent the resulting alloy is rendered too brittle for any practical purpose. Below 4 percent copper content, the alloy is subject to hot tearing; above 5 percent this problem diminishes. At conditions of equilibrium about 5.6 percent, copper is soluble at 1018 degrees Fahrenheit; at room temperature the solubility of copper is less than 1/2 percent. *Equilibrium* is the state of balance between opposing forces or effects.

When copper is added to pure aluminum, it results in one of

the best known precipitation hardening systems. In chilled aluminum-copper alloy castings and properly heat-treated castings, the copper constituent is very finely divided, resulting in a nearly continuous solid solution of copper and aluminum. In other words, the copper and aluminum are very evenly mixed together, giving you both strength and hardness, a good homogeneous structure. Copper and aluminum react together to form an intermetallic compound; this compound forms a solid solution. The amount of copper in an aluminum alloy will vary from .05 percent to as high as 10.7 percent.

A very popular general casting aluminum alloy years ago was called aluminum alloy #12. It was 92 percent pure aluminum and 8 percent copper. When the mix was 90 percent aluminum and 10 percent copper, it was called ingot #21. In fact, when I first worked in the foundry, when the customer simply wanted an aluminum casting requiring no particular pedigree what he got was old #12. If we had the ingot on hand we went this way; if not, we made a heat of pure aluminum and added the proper percent of 50/50 aluminum-copper hardener to give us #12 or #21 or somewhere in between. The straight aluminum and copper alloys were not the best actors in regard to ease of castings and were not nearly as fluid as alloys containing some silicon, but we made do.

SILICON

Silicon greatly improves the foundry characteristics of aluminum. With the addition of silicon, the fluidity of the alloy jumps in leaps and bounds along with a decrease in hot tearing problems. There is also a pronounced reduction in volumetric shrinkage, thus eliminating many shrinkage problems and reducing the number of gates and risers that are needed. This shrinkage reduction can be as much as 50 percent less than pure aluminum. Silicon can be added up to the eutectic point, which is approximately 12.6 percent silicon. Silicon aluminum will produce fine-grained, pressure-tight castings.

The eutectic point is reached when two or more substances capable of forming a solid solution with each other have the property of lowering each other's freezing point; the minimum freeze point which can be obtained corresponding to the eutectic mixture is called its *eutectic point*. In this case, 87.4 percent aluminum and 12.6 percent silicon would be the percent mix resulting in the lowest freezing point of the alloy. Less than 12.6 percent silicon would make the alloy freeze, or solidify, at a higher temperature. More than 12.6 percent silicon would not decrease the freezing point any further than 12.6 percent would. Now, if you lower the solidification point, you increase the range over which the alloy is liquid; this is called the *solidification range*. When you do this, you are able to pour thinner sections easily and get away with smaller risers, because the metal in the risers will stay liquid over a longer temperature span, allowing them to provide liquid metal to the solidifying casting easily. In other words, pure aluminum goes from a liquid to a solid over a much shorter temperature span than would an alloy of aluminum and silicon.

When the silicon content is very high, the castings lose ductility and also become tougher to machine, often requiring the use of carbide-tipped tooling. The high end of silicon in aluminum is about 13 percent. Silicon is soluble to 1.65 percent in aluminum at the solidification point of 1070 degrees Fahrenheit; at room temperature this figure is .1 percent.

MAGNESIUM

Magnesium up to 6 percent will strengthen aluminum. Above this point, the strength is no longer increased; however the hardness will increase. Magnesium aluminum alloys have good machinability and good corrosion resistance. Alloys with more than 6 percent magnesium are heat-treatable.

When magnesium is added to an alloy of aluminum and silicon, a compound of magnesium and silicon is formed, called magnesium silicide. Because this compound is soluble at about 1.85 percent at 1103 degrees Fahrenheit, maximum properties are obtained by heat-treating them. Approximately 15 percent of magnesium is soluble in aluminum at 844 degrees Fahrenheit, and less than 2½ percent at room temperature.

Now, as with any alloy which contains magnesium, there is a tendency for the magnesium to dross, producing bad castings if proper gating is not practiced. The metal must enter the mold cavity with minimum agitation, by simple displacement, preferably through a horn gate (Fig. 2-1). Aside from dross problems, magnesium-aluminum alloys have a short solidification range, so you are faced with careful planning in respect to the use of heavy risers and chill or the combination of the two.

IRON

Iron is considered by most as an undesirable impurity, but ac-

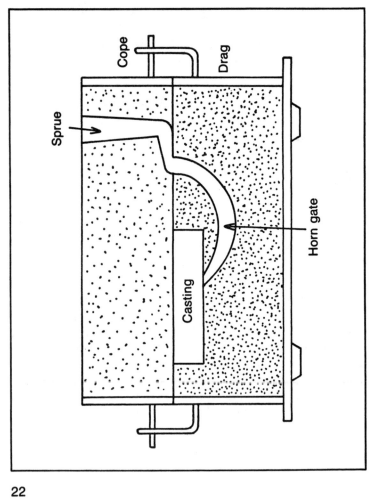

Fig. 2-1. Horn gate.

tually it is somewhat beneficial. It will increase the hardness and strength of some alloys. In alloys designed to be cast in permanent molds, and in aluminum die casting, you will find it common to have an iron percentage as high as 1 percent. The iron reduces *soldering,* which occurs when the aluminum cast into the die or permold actually welds, or solders, itself to the die cavity. Also it is difficult not to pick up some iron by the solvent action from skimmer bars and other iron accessories which come in contact with the molten aluminum. For years casters used steel wool in the sprue to act as a strainer to prevent inclusions such as aluminum oxide, slag, or sand in the casting. It did an excellent job (Fig. 2-2). The return melt, gates, sprues, etc. were kept to a ratio of not more than ⅓ of the total melt against ingot.

Now on the market are ceramic filters which will remove extremely fine oxides and nonmetallic particulates, preventing them from entering the molds and thus becoming entrapped in the casting. These filters, called Selee filters, are available from Consolidated Aluminum Corporation (Fig. 2-3).

Other sources of iron particulates are unlined steel ladles and melting kettles. Although they are usually coated with a protective wash, such as koline (kiln wash) or chalk, you can get some contamination (Fig. 2-4).

Don't take this as a free license to contaminate the melt with iron. In general, the properties of a given alloy are progressively deteriorated as the dissolved iron content is increased.

Iron and aluminum form the compound Al_3Fe. The eutectic point is at 1.7 percent iron with a solidification point of 1211 degrees Fahrenheit.

MANGANESE

Small amounts of manganese are found in some complex aluminum alloys. About 1.8 percent of manganese is soluble in aluminum at 1217 degrees Fahrenheit, but at room temperature it drops to .3 percent.

ZINC

In the early days of aluminum casting, binary alloys of aluminum and zinc were widely used. They were difficult to cast and very susceptible to stress corrosion, increased density, and low strength at elevated temperatures. These older alloys ran in ex-

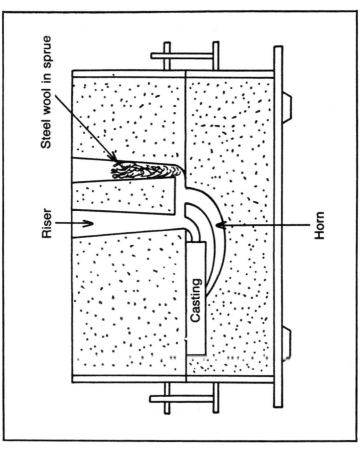

Fig. 2-2. Steel-wool strainer in down sprue.

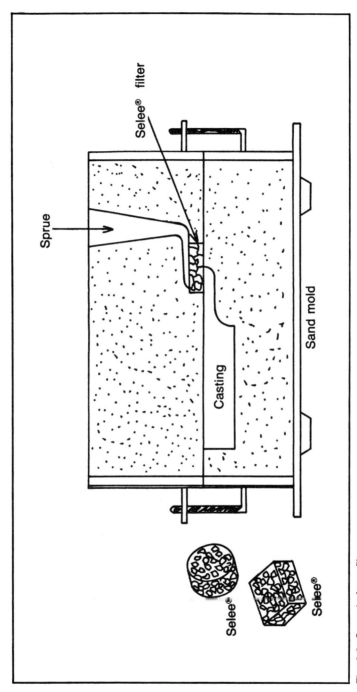

Fig. 2-3. Ceramic foam filter.

25

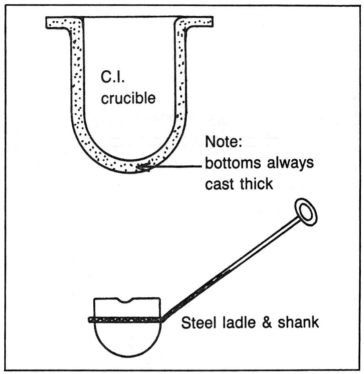

Fig. 2-4. Cast-iron melting kettle with a crucible, unlined, steel ladle.

cess of 10 percent zinc. Up to 3 percent zinc in an aluminum alloy has little effect on its properties.

At its solidification point of 825 degrees Fahrenheit, 84 percent of zinc is soluble in solid aluminum. This solubility drops to 2 percent at room temperature.

Old Alloys. Let's look at some of the old alloys that were high in zinc.

Alloy 31 was 80.5 percent Al, 16 percent Zn, 3 percent Cu, and .5 percent Mn. Alloy 34 was 78 percent Al and 22 percent Zn. Old Airplane piston alloy from World War I was 80.97 percent Al, 15.16 percent Zn, 1.9 percent Cu, 1.06 percent Fe, and 45 percent Si.

Exceptions to the rule on keeping the zinc below 3 percent include some high-strength (as-cast) alloys, such as tenzaloy, an alloy produced by Federated Metals. It has a zinc content from 4 to 8 percent. In these complex alloys, the zinc will form with other elements to produce intermetallic compounds which help provide the alloy's excellent characteristics.

Tenzaloy. The nominal composition of tenzaloy is: 91.5 percent aluminum, 0.6 percent copper, 7.5 percent zinc, and 0.4 percent magnesium. Tenzaloy weighs 0.1 pound per cubic inch, and the pattern-maker's shrinkage is 5/32 inch to the foot for small castings and 7/32 inch to the foot for large castings. The pouring temperature most commonly used is between 1275 and 1400 degrees Fahrenheit. Degassing agents that contain chlorine will remove the magnesium. The basis of most solid aluminum flux sold to foundries is zinc chloride.

If you use this type of flux, use only a small amount when melting an alloy containing magnesium—only 1 teaspoon per 50 pounds of melt.

Tenzaloy is basically a sand-cast aluminum that develops high strength at room temperature; so it does not require heat treating (along with its cost). This alloy has a tensile strength of 29,000 PSI as-cast after 1 day at room temperature. After 10 to 14 days at room temperature, the tensile strength jumps to 35,000 PSI. If you are in a hurry, you can age it at 250 degrees Fahrenheit for 10 to 16 hours to get the 35,000 PSI tensile strength.

The brinell hardness jumps from 60 as-cast for 1 day, to 74 after 10 to 14 days at room temperature or 10 to 16 hours at 250 degrees Fahrenheit. Generally speaking, the best combination of properties are achieved by simply letting the castings set at room temperature for the 10 to 14 days, rather than artificially aging them at 250 degrees Fahrenheit.

It is not my purpose to endorse any particular product, but I have cast a lot of tenzaloy, and it is a great alloy. It has, however, a rather short solidification range; so it requires larger risers and gates.

NICKEL

Nickel is used chiefly in complex alloys. The main purpose for its use, regardless of the percentage, is to allow the casting to retain as much of its strength as possible at elevated temperatures. The total percentage runs from less than 1 percent to a maximum of about 2 percent. Binary aluminum-nickel alloys are available in percentage grades up to 80 percent aluminum and 20 percent nickel. They are used as master alloys for compounding aluminum alloys when you want a percentage of nickel. Nickel forms a eutectic point with aluminum at 1184 degree Fahrenheit when the content is 5.7 percent nickel. At room temperature, the solid solution of nickel in aluminum is only .01 percent.

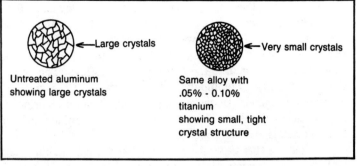

Untreated aluminum showing large crystals ← Large crystals

Same alloy with .05% - 0.10% titanium showing small, tight crystal structure ← Very small crystals

Fig. 2-5. Micrograph showing the grain-refining benefits of titanium.

TITANIUM

The use of titanium as an element in aluminum is as a grain refiner. For optimum grain refinement, only a minor percentage is required—.05 to .1 percent. It is extremely useful for pressure-tight castings (Fig. 2-5).

Ingots which contain titanium are available for casting; however, melting these ingots down for casting results in a reduction of the grain-refining properties produced by titanium. Therefore, if you wish maximum grain refinement through the use of titanium, you should add the titanium in the form of an aluminum-titanium master alloy shortly before you pour the castings. A master alloy is available for this purpose in a range of from 2.5 to 5 percent titanium-aluminum remainder and 6 to 10 percent titanium-aluminum remainder. Master alloys will be further discussed in later chapters.

3

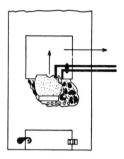

Aluminum Melting Furnaces and Devices

Now, this chapter might seem like I am putting the cart before the horse; however, you must have some sort of a melting furnace or device before you begin to cast. Aluminum melting devices come in all sorts of designs and configurations because aluminum—with its low melting and casting temperatures as compared to brass, iron, or steel—is easily melted. This makes aluminum a good backyard—casting metal, because it does not require expensive and complicated melting rigs.

Because the maximum pouring temperature would never exceed 1500 degrees Fahrenheit, but would be more in the range of 1200 to 1500 degrees Fahrenheit (compared with red metals at pouring temperatures from 2100 to 2300 degrees Fahrenheit and gray iron between 2600 and 2800 degrees Fahrenheit), molten aluminum is quite cold. You can melt aluminum in a furnace which is fueled by gas, fuel oil, coke, or electricity. Let's explore some melting devices.

THE CHIMNEY FURNACE

The chimney, or smoke stack, is a powerful device. Tall chimneys were very common in the United States during the Industrial Revolution and before government regulatory agencies came into being. Contrary to popular belief, these huge stacks were not a simple method to direct the smoke, fly ash, heat, fumes, etc., to great heights so that they could blow away and later settle on distant neighbors. These chimneys were built and very carefully engineered to produce a given draft and were rated in horsepower capacity. The *capacity* of a chimney is the theoretical amount of fuel it will burn during a stated interval, and consequently the theoretical amount of gasses it will pass in the same time.

The general requirement for a chimney is first to provide draft and thereby produce combustion of a fuel, and secondly to carry away the products of combustion. The first requirement, the draft, is governed by the height, and the second requirement is governed by the diameter (ID) of the chimney. Thus the taller the chimney, the more draft it will produce, generating more products of combustion and requiring more inside area to carry away these products of combustion. The *draft* is the difference in pressure produced by the difference in weight between the hot gasses inside the chimney and the equivalent column of outside air. The intensity of the draft is measured in inches of water and is determined theoretically by the following formula:

$$D = 0.518 \text{ Po } H \left[\frac{1}{To} - \frac{1}{Tc} \right]$$

Where D = Draft in inches of water.
      H = Height of the chimney in feet.
    Po = Observed atmospheric pressure in pounds per square inch.
    To = Absolute temperature of the outside temperature in degrees Fahrenheit.
    Tc = Absolute temperature of the chimney gasses in degrees Fahrenheit.

Of course there are various other factors, such as loss due to the friction in the chimney and loss due to velocity in inches of water. One inch of water would equal 0.58 ounces per square inch of pressure. Let's look at a few chimney horsepower ratings used on height and inside diameter for a chimney 100 feet tall of various inside diameters at sea level:

100' tall at 6 1/4' in diameter = 1000 HP.
100' tall at 3 1/2' in diameter = 250 HP.
100' tall at 4 1/2' in diameter = 500 HP.

Converted into energy, the 1000 horsepower chimney would equal 746 kilowatt hours, 1.98 billion foot pounds, or 2.545 million BTUs (British thermal units) per hour. Based on 100 percent efficiency, it takes about 517 BTUs to melt 1 pound of aluminum; so the 1000 horsepower chimney would melt 4922.6 pounds of aluminum every hour.

This information is simply to demonstrate that all you need to melt aluminum is some fuel to combust and a chimney to provide the necessary oxygen to carry out that combustion. The relationship between the height of a chimney and its inside diameter to its horsepower rating is provided to help you with a problem chimney. Note: home fireplace chimneys are usually very poorly designed.

MAKING YOUR OWN FURNACE

If you hang a piece of pipe in a tree which is 12 inches in diameter and 12 feet tall, you will be surprised how much aluminum you can melt very quickly using charcoal briquettes, coal, or coke. The amount of fuel needed to melt and superheat 100 pounds of aluminum follows: bituminous coal, 4.3 pounds—anthracite coal, 3.7 pounds—coke or charcoal, 4.0 pounds—natural gas, 57.0 cubic feet—fuel oil, 2.7 pounds. The amounts are averages when the melted aluminum is superheated to 1472 degrees Fahrenheit.

Get yourself a piece of pipe 12 feet long with about a 12-inch inside diameter and a wall thickness of no less than 3/16 inch. Come up about 4 inches from the bottom and drill six holes across the diameter to take 1/2-inch re-rods for a grate. You can, if you like, burn these holes with a cutting torch. Now cut six 1/2-inch re-rods and insert them through the holes to form the grate. Weld them in place and burn off the ends. See Fig. 3-1.

Now cut out a section of the pipe below the grate 3 inches high by 6 inches long (Fig. 3-2). This gives you an ash clean-out opening. Now fabricate a door for this opening. See Fig. 3-3.

For the area above the grate, you must make an opening similar to the ash-pit opening so you can place your crucible or cast-iron melting pot on a brick pedestal on the grate. The height of this opening above the grate depends upon the size of the crucible, as does its overall width and height. This opening is also provided with a hinged door and a simple latch to keep it closed when you are melting aluminum (Fig. 3-4).

The bottom of this opening is just a fraction below the top of

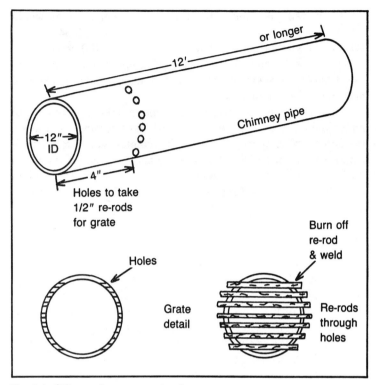

Fig. 3-1. Chimney furnace construction.

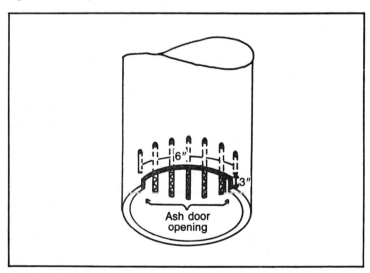

Fig. 3-2. Chimney furnace construction continued—ash opening door.

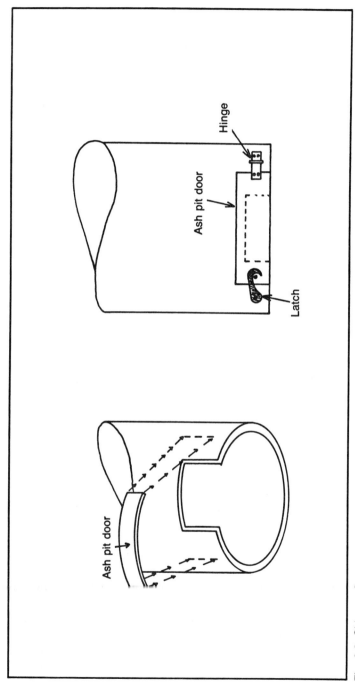

Fig. 3-3. Chimney furnace construction continued—ash pit door.

33

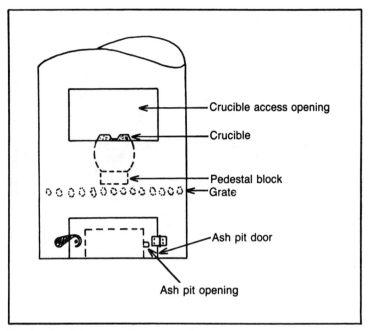

Fig. 3-4. Crucible access furnace opening.

the chosen crucible or melting pot when it is resting on a 2-inch pedestal which is resting on the grate. The height and width of this opening are large enough to allow you to remove the crucible with the pouring tongs. See Fig. 3-5.

Assume you will use a #10 crucible, which is 8 1/16 inches tall and 6 9/16 inches at the bilge. This crucible will have a melt capacity of 10 pounds aluminum or 30 pounds brass. In order to remove this crucible easily and safely from the chimney furnace, you will need an opening approximately 10 inches wide by 12 inches tall (Fig. 3-6). The opening to retrieve the crucible is, like the ash pit, provided with a simple hinged door with a latch. For the bottom, which is simply a round steel plate welded to the bottom, see Fig. 3-7.

To control the draft, you can simply cock the ash pit's door ajar, or provide an adjustable draft opening in the back below the grate or on the bottom plate. See Fig. 3-8. The chimney furnace is hung in a tree or a suitable legged frame. If it is hung in a tree, the chimney must be guyed to prevent it from swinging (Fig. 3-9).

You have a lot of leeway in the construction of a chimney melter as to design, support, diameter, etc.; however, a chimney shorter than 10 feet will not draw enough air to burn the fuel with enough heat to do the job. You can also, if you choose, put a butterfly damper in the chimney above the melting zone for additional control. See Fig. 3-10.

Another innovation is to insulate the melting area with castable refractory, plastic firebrick, or a 50/50 mix of fireclay and silica sand. This insulation will greatly increase the efficiency of your melter and reduce the time it takes to melt a heat. See Fig. 3-11. Another method is shown in Fig. 3-12.

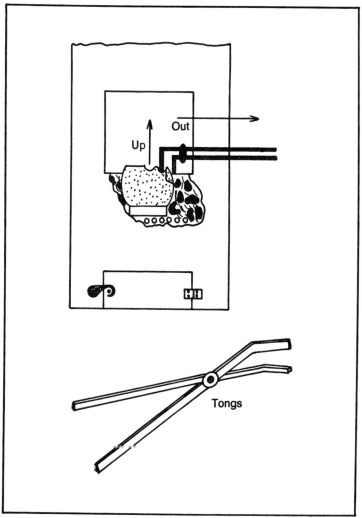

Fig. 3-5. Removing the crucible with bent-leg tongs.

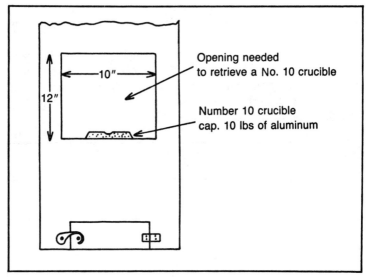

Fig. 3-6. Opening suitable for a #10 crucible.

MELTING WITH A FURNACE

Melting with the chimney furnace is simplicity itself. You simply place the crucible charged with the aluminum on the pedestal block. Place a piece of cardboard between the crucible bottom and the pedestal block to prevent the crucible from attaching itself to the pedestal during the heat. Now simply fill in the area between the crucible and lining or chimney with coke, charcoal, or coal. See Fig. 3-13.

There are several ways to light off. You can place a layer of light wood kindling and paper in first and the fuel on top, or you can use charcoal lighter fluid. To assist in getting things going, you can blow into the ash pit's door with a hand bellows.

As the fuel burns down, add fresh fuel to replace the burned fuel. Keep the fuel level to the top of the crucible. Adjust the draft to the point where you have ½ to 1 inch of blue flames coming off the top of the fuel bed.

You will be surprised as to how fast this unit will melt down a pot of aluminum. As the aluminum melts down, add dry, fresh scrap aluminum to the crucible. Let this melt and add more until the crucible is full. Allow sufficient room between the crucible top and the metal level to accommodate the pouring tongs (Fig. 3-14). You can also melt red brass, silicon bronze, and zinc in your chimney furnace.

36

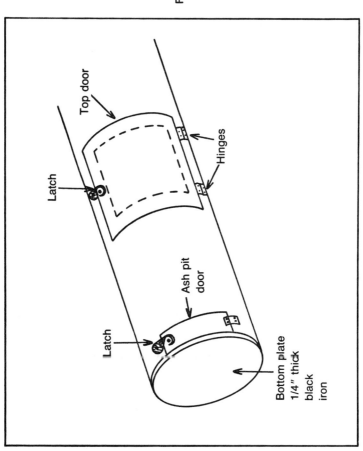

Fig. 3-7. Bottom plate on a chimney furnace.

Top door

Latch

Hinges

Latch

Ash pit door

Bottom plate
1/4" thick
black
iron

37

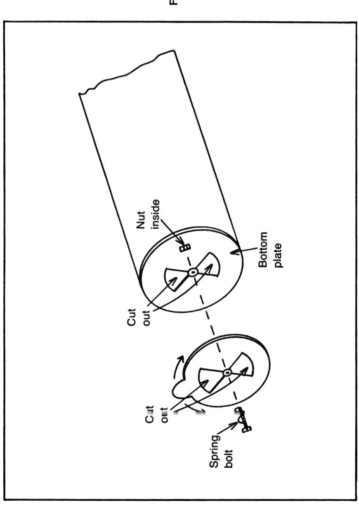

Fig. 3-8. Rotary draft plate.

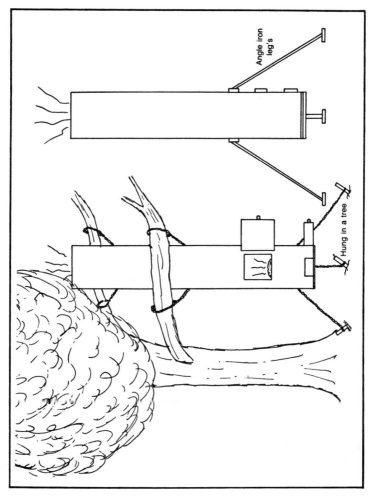

Fig. 3-9. Chimney furnace support methods.

Angle iron leg's

Hung in a tree

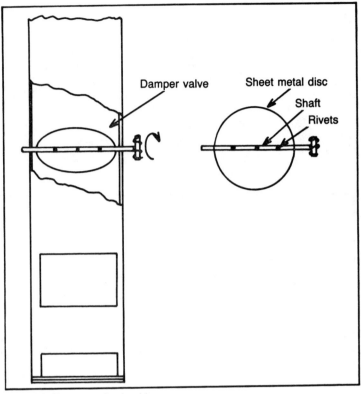

Fig. 3-10. Damper valve in chimney.

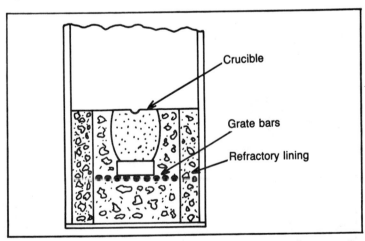

Fig. 3-11. Refractory-lined melting zone of chimney furnace increases the efficiency.

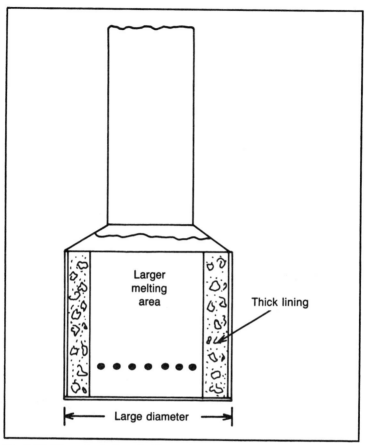

Fig. 3-12. Alternate design of chimney furnace in order to accommodate a thicker refractory lining and/or a larger crucible.

When the pot is full to the desired level, let the aluminum superheat to a very dull red. Remove the crucible with the tongs, skim, and pour. You might have to pick out some of the fuel with the tongs to get a good grip on the crucible. If you wish to start another heat right away, remove the fuel piece by piece with the tongs and place the burning fuel in a 5-gallon steel bucket. Put the crucible back on the pedestal and return the hot fuel around the crucible. Add fresh fuel to the top, load the crucible with aluminum, and you are off again.

If you are finished, remove the fuel, place it in a bucket, and quench it out with water. Set it aside to dry and use the unburned fuel as additional fuel on the next heat you run. If you wish, you

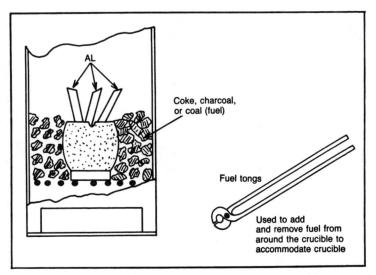

Fig. 3-13. Chimney furnace ready to light.

can fill the melt area full of coke or blacksmith's coal up to the bottom of the come-out door (leaving the crucible out), and use your chimney melter as a very handy blacksmith's forge for small work.

You can, if you like, melt aluminum in a cast-iron plumber's

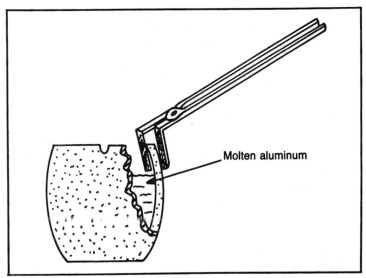

Fig. 3-14. Leave space for the inside leg of come-out tongs between molten aluminum and the top of the crucible.

pot and ladle out the aluminum to pour. This arrangement is great for casting small parts. See Fig. 3-15.

Let's look at another arrangement of a solid fuel melter which uses natural draft. The setup in Fig. 3-16 operates the same way as a chimney melter does. The advantage is that it gives easy top access to fuel and the crucible.

RIVET FORGE

You can melt brass, bronze, or aluminum in a simple rivet forge, which you can find from time to time in a junk yard. You can also simply build one for yourself out of a circular charcoal grill. The rivet forge does not have a stack or chimney to produce the draft to combust the fuel. The draft is supplied by a blower which blows through a single bottom tuyere, or nozzle, to supply the necessary oxygen to convert the carbon in the fuel to carbon monoxide and carbon dioxide to produce the heat. You must either motorize the blower or turn the blower handle manually. See Fig. 3-17.

To convert the rivet forge, you line a 5-gallon metal bucket with

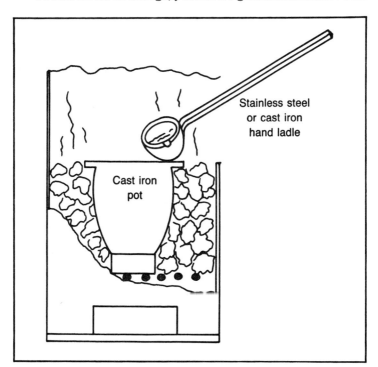

Stainless steel or cast iron hand ladle

Cast iron pot

Fig. 3-15. A chimney furnace used as a dip-out furnace with C.I. pot.

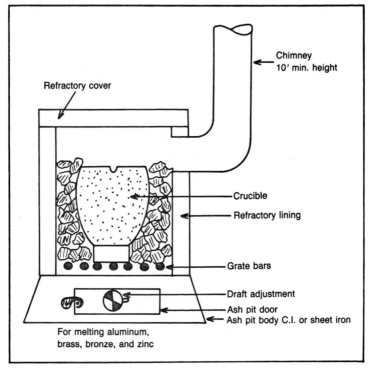

Fig. 3-16. Another solid-fuel, natural-draft melter.

refractory such as A.P. Green castable insulation No. 20, a good, cheap material for this purpose and easy to use. See Fig. 3-18.

Now you simply place the crucible on two split bricks to span the central tuyere. Build up under and around the crucible with the fuel. Start the fire, supplying a little air from the blower through the tuyere to get it started. When all the fuel is red throughout, put the lined bucket over the loaded crucible and turn the blower at a medium speed. Very quickly you will have a potful ready to pour.

For the furnace shown in Fig. 3-16, if you wish to melt very fast, supply a blower below the grate. The blower provides forced draft, resulting in much faster and hotter combustion. See Fig. 3-19. If you go this route, you can eliminate most of your chimney height.

A REVERBERATORY FURNACE

Let's look at the general construction of a simple, shallow-hearth, natural-draft, reverberatory furnace. See Fig. 3-20. In this

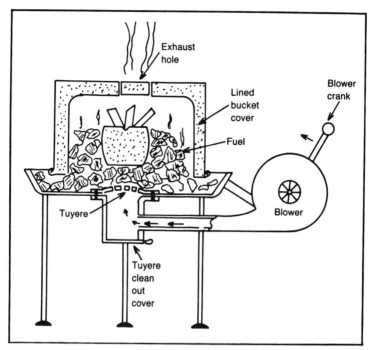

Fig. 3-17. Rivet-forge aluminum melter.

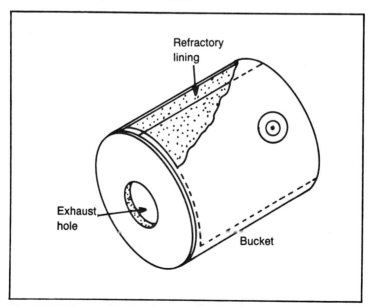

Fig. 3-18. Refractory-lined bucket cover for rivet forge melter.

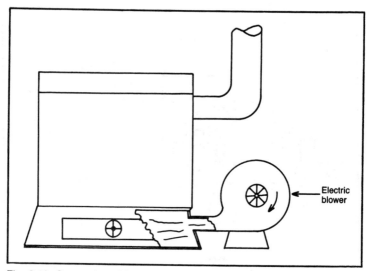

Fig. 3-19. Conversion of furnace to a forced-draft melter.

arrangement, the fuel is burned on a grate, and the hot gasses are drawn through the melting chamber by the draft of the chimney. The material to be melted is charged into the throat of the stack where it melts, runs down on to the hearth, and is superheated by the radiant heat of the furnace roof.

The floor of the hearth is sloped in every direction to a tap hole, which is plugged with a bott. When sufficient metal is melted and superheated for the job at hand, the bott is picked out with a tapping bar, and the molten metal runs into the pouring ladle. The arrangement is often modified to provide an outside well from which the metal can be dipped out with hand ladles for pouring. In this case, the tap hole is not included, and the molten metal in the well is at the same level as the hearth metal level (Fig. 3-21).

OTHER FURNACES

Figure 3-22 shows the details of a small, but very efficient, dip-out aluminum melting furnace which is fired by natural gas. This furnace was built by my friend, Sam Pitre Jr. Sam used this furnace for years to cast thousands of aluminum fan spiders in a permanent cast-iron mold of his design and construction. Sam melted mostly scrap aluminum pistons purchased from auto rebuilders and junkyards.

There are all sorts of novel arrangements; one of which is a

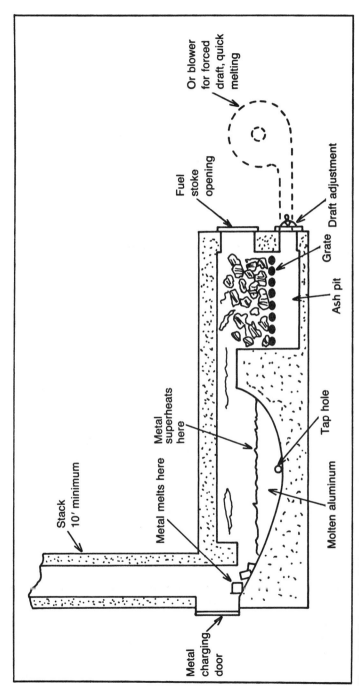

Fig. 3-20. Flat-roof, solid-fuel, natural-draft, reverberatory furnace.

47

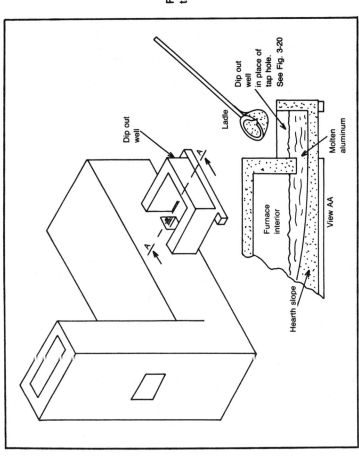

Fig. 3-21. Dip-out well arrangement in lieu of tap hole.

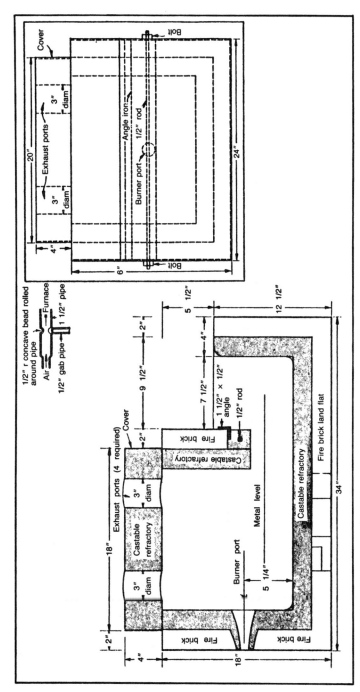

Fig. 3-22. Dip-out® gas-fired box furnace.

49

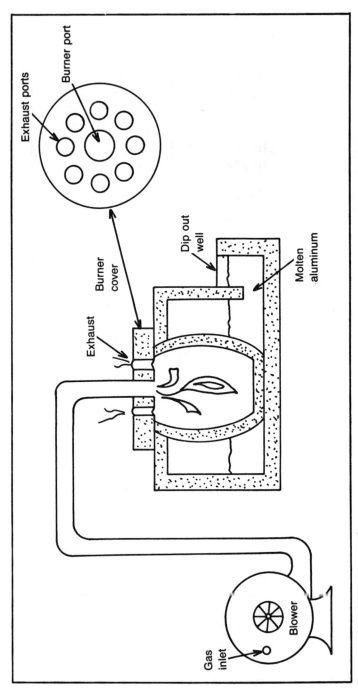

Fig. 3-23. Novel aluminum melter.

gas-fired, noncrucible furnace in which the aluminum does not come in contact with the products of combustion. In this arrangement, a large crucible is set on the furnace hearth. The burner is fired down into the interior of the crucible and comes back out through a series of exhaust holes around a cover fitted to the crucible's top. The crucible gets hot, and the heat radiated from the outside of the crucible melts the aluminum. See Fig. 3-23.

The standard gas- or oil-fired crucible furnace is always a good bet. This can be a stationary or a tilting furnace, homemade or purchased. A stationary cast-iron melting pot, dip-out type, or cast-iron pit tilt furnace, either gas- or oil-fired, is also a good choice. Cast-iron melting pots are available in all sizes and shapes. The most common is the round, flanged type for a stationary dip-out furnace. See Figs. 3-24 through 3-26.

If I were starting up a small hobby or jobbing cast-aluminum operation, I would go for the stationary, cast-iron pot type of furnace fired with natural gas or propane. If I expected to run a large variety of aluminum alloys, I would choose a standard, stationary, graphite-crucible, lift-out furnace and use a separate crucible for each alloy to prevent cross contamination.

If I was handling basically one type of alloy or scrap, I would design the furnace based on maximum casting size and turn a pattern for my cast-iron pot or shop for a gray-iron foundry to cast my pot and build the furnace to fit it.

Figure 3-27 can be used as a general guideline for a lift-out crucible furnace, or you can modify the furnace to take a flanged cast-iron melting pot by deleting the cover and providing side exhaust.

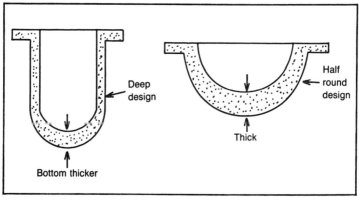

Fig. 3-24. Cast-iron melting pots.

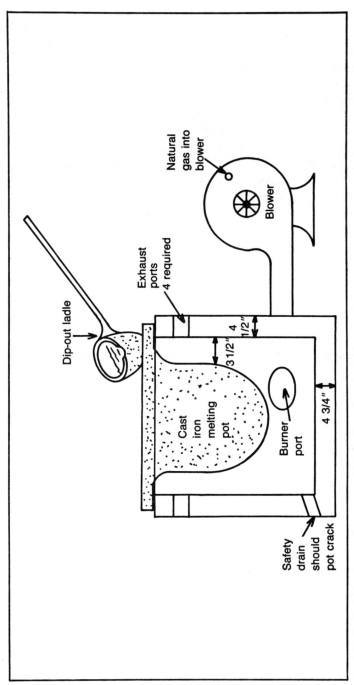

Fig. 3-25. Basic design for cast-iron pot used for aluminum in a dip-out furnace.

Natural gas into blower

Blower

Exhaust ports 4 required

Dip-out ladle

Cast iron melting pot

Burner port

4 1/2"

3 1/2"

4 3/4"

Safety drain should pot crack

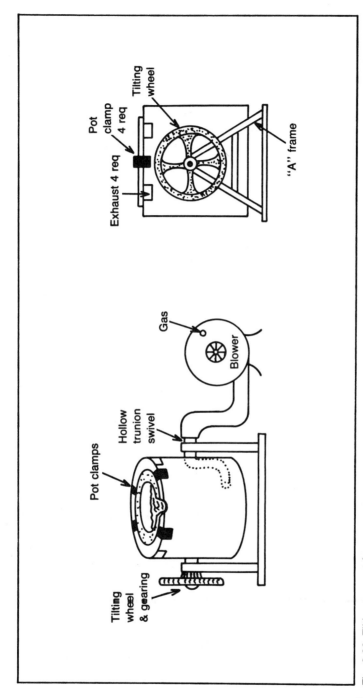

Fig. 3-26. Tilting iron-pot furnace.

53

Actually just about any arrangement will work, even a bucket of charcoal with draft supplied by an old hair blower or vacuum cleaner. For additional furnace construction, see *The Complete Handbook of Sand Casting* (TAB Book No. 1043).

CHOICE AND CONSIDERATIONS

It is impossible to simply state what you should build or buy to meet your melting requirement, because there are so many variables involved. Your prime considerations are the requirements of the foundry and the fuel or power available at the most economical cost. If you are considering a general jobbing foundry where you intend to run a variety of different alloys at different weights, your best bet would be one or more lift-out stationary crucible furnaces. If you will basically run the same alloy most of the time over a long run, then your choice might be an electric induction furnace or a gas-fired reverberatory furnace.

Another factor is what size or casting you are going to be pouring. What weight range is it? You must choose a furnace which has the capacity to pour the largest casting and has the risers and gates that you intend to run. A small two- or three-man shop should decide on a fairly definite weight and size limit and stick to it. Let the jobs that are too large in size or weight go to the foundry with this capacity. How much metal is needed each day? Choose a furnace which makes it possible to pour the molten metal as soon as it is ready.

If you are pouring castings for your own amazement or for prototype work, models, or just a hobby, the choice is much simpler. Crucible furnaces are the easiest to build and easiest to use. Induction furnaces are expensive, and unless you are in an area where you can buy the power at a very low rate, they cannot be operated economically. Reverberatory furnaces are tricky to operate. The large, shallow metal bath exposes a large area of the melt to the products of combustion, which can result in excessive oxidation and gas absorption. It is also difficult to degas a large, shallow bath or add master alloys uniformly throughout the melt.

Last, but not least, you can make a slick melter, where the metal is actually melted in the pouring ladle. These furnaces can be purchased, and are used in some pattern shops to melt aluminum to cast patterns, core boxes, dryers, etc. See Fig. 3-28.

The melting pot or ladle is made of stainless steel or black iron pipe with a pouring lip on top and a welded bottom. The shank ring is secured to the ladle with set screws. The ladle with shank at-

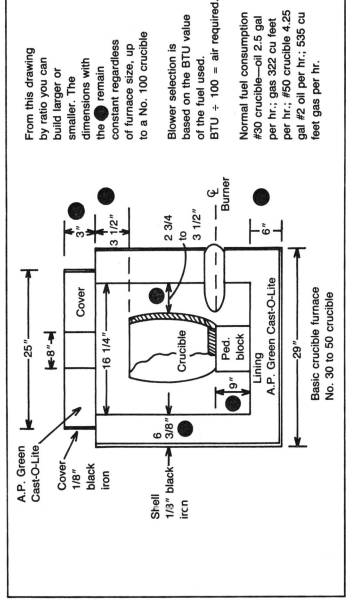

From this drawing by ratio you can build larger or smaller. The dimensions with the ● remain constant regardless of furnace size, up to a No. 100 crucible

Blower selection is based on the BTU value of the fuel used.
BTU ÷ 100 = air required.

Normal fuel consumption #30 crucible—oil 2.5 gal per hr.; gas 322 cu feet per hr.; #50 crucible 4.25 gal #2 oil per hr.; 535 cu feet gas per hr.

3"
3 1/2"

Cover

25"

8"

16 1/4"

2 3/4 to 3 1/2"

₵ Burner

A.P. Green Cast-O-Lite

Cover
1/8" black iron

6 3/8"

Shell
1/3" black ircn

Crucible

Ped. block

9"

Lining
A.P. Green Cast-O-Lite

29"

6"

Basic crucible furnace
No. 30 to 50 crucible

Fig. 3-27. Guideline for building a basic lift-out crucible furnace for melting aluminum or brass.

55

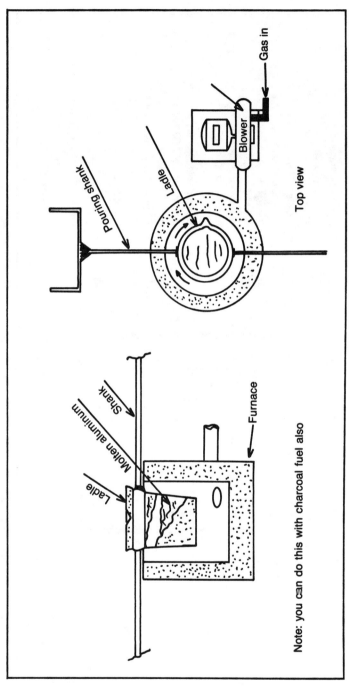

Gas in

Blower

Pouring shank

Ladle

Top view

Shank

Molten aluminum

Ladle

Furnace

Note: you can do this with charcoal fuel also

Fig. 3-28. A melt in the ladle furnace.

tached is simply set in the furnace. The shank holds it in the proper position. It is charged, and when the metal is ready to pour, you simply lift it out by the shank.

I built a melt pouring rig out of a piece of regular seamless pipe ¼ inch wall and 10-inch inside diameter and coated the inside with a wash of graphite and water glass (silicate of soda). It lasted approximately 200 heats before it gave up.

CRUCIBLES

The cost of graphite and silicon carbide crucibles has gone through the roof in the last 10 to 15 years. So for you who are purest do-it-yourselfers, a few old-time formulas for crucibles are given in Table 3-1. Perhaps your local art potter will help you here. If you can come up with some nice melting crucibles of good quality, there is no doubt that you could sell all you wished to fellow hobby founders.

Table 3-1. Formulas for Crucibles.

Mix Number	Ingredients	Use
#1.	1 part fireclay 1 part grog peak sized canister) 1 part graphite (parts by weight)	Use for melting brass, bronze & aluminum.
#2.	1 part fireclay 2 parts graphite (parts by weight)	Use multimetals.
#3.	7 parts by volume fireclay 8 parts by volume burnt clay	Hand-built melting crucible.
#4.	6 parts by volume fireclay 3 parts by volume grog 4 parts by volume burnt clay	Hand-built crucibles.
#5.	Water 8 qts. Tenn. ball clay 18 lbs. Sodium silicate (waterglass) 2oz. Mullite 200 mesh 21 lbs. Mullite 325 mesh 21 lbs.	The above mix is for slip casting crucibles to be used for multi-melting and glass melting.

#6.	A.P. Green, Mo. fire clay 4 parts by vol. Tenn. #9 clay 2 parts by vol. A.P. Green fine grog.
	    4 parts by vol. mullite
	    4 parts by vol. water as little as possible.
		This mix is for hand-built crucibles for multimetal melting.

57

4

Fuels

The first consideration in choosing the right fuel for your operation would be the availability and cost in your particular locality. Natural gas and oil are both available in most localities. Let's examine the two.

OIL VS. NATURAL GAS

In order to compare the cost of oil and natural gas, you simply compare the thermal value, or *BTU content*, of each against cost. Actually what you are buying is energy, or BTUs.

Let's say that oil contains a heat value of 130,000 BTUs per gallon. Because as natural gas is about 1,000 BTUs per cubic foot, 1 gallon of oil is equal to 130 cubic feet of gas. So, if 1 gallon of oil costs the same as 130 cubic feet of natural gas, we would be even.

In order to avoid large numbers, most fuel is sold by the *therm*, which the practical unit of the quantity of heat. One therm equals 100,000 BTUs, 25.2 million calories, or about 105.5 million joules. Therefore, 100 cubic feet of natural gas at a BTU value of 1,000 BTUs per cubic feet would equal 1 therm of heat energy.

The amount of heat needed to melt is calculated by the formula:

$$W = T \times Sm\ (0\text{-}T) + R.$$

Where W = The total heat required in gram calories.

T = melting point in degrees centigrade from 0.

Sm (0-T) = is the specific heat between 0 centigrade and
   T degrees centigrade.

R = latent heat of fusion in gram calories.

This formula is based on pure aluminum raised from 0 degrees Centigrade. Aluminum, however, is not normally at 0 degrees Centigrade, but is at room temperature above 25 degrees Centigrade (77 degrees Fahrenheit) and is normally an alloy with a melting temperature a bit lower than pure aluminum. For all practical purposes, then, we want to know how many therms it takes to get the aluminum from 77 degrees Fahrenheit to its melting point, and how many more therms to get to a superheat of 800 degrees Centigrade, or 1472 degrees Fahrenheit, which is about the average pouring temperature.

It will take us 243.9 calories to get from room temperature to 658.7 degrees Centigrade to melting point. Now we need some extra calories to drive it up to 800 degrees Centigrade pouring temperature. It takes 517 BTUs per pound to raise the aluminum from room temperature to the average pouring temperature of 1472 degrees Fahrenheit.

At 517 BTUs per pound, if we had 100 pounds to melt and superheat, we need 51,700 BTUs to do this job. If 1 therm is equal to 100,000 BTUs, then it would take us 0.517 therm to melt the 100 pounds, and bring it to pouring temperature, or .00517 therms per pound. So all you need to know is how much per therm gas or oil costs, and the companies will quote by the therm.

Now remember, your cost per therm should be figured at the furnace burner adding in all other costs, such as hauling the oil or coke to you, or your cost of going after it, as well as the cost of maintenance, crucibles, etc. Also, these calculations are based on 100 percent efficiency, which you don't ever have. Some therms are going to get away from you. You are not going to be able to cram every one of the 100,000 BTUs in each therm into the aluminum. In time, by keeping records, you will be in a better position to figure how much your melting is really costing per pound melted against per pound of salable casting weight.

OIL

Just about any grade of fuel oil can be burned. Of course if the specific gravity is too high, you will need to heat the oil in order to get it to flow and atomized at the burner. The problem will increase in cold weather.

An oil of about 28 to 30 degrees Baumé, which is sold as #3 fuel oil, is preferred. This grade of oil is light enough to flow readily at all ordinary temperatures and is easily atomized by the burner. It's a give and take proposition. If you buy a cheaper oil, say #5, the BTUs or therms will cost you less, but the problems of lower efficiency of combustion, heating, and poorer atomization will soon wipe out your cost per therm saving.

Of course you can use automobile crankcase drainings, but they must be filtered to remove the solid sludge and dirt. Most people who go this route have a very cheap source of this oil, such as a friend with a gas station. They usually thin the oil out with kerosene to get into the 28 to 30 degrees *Baumé scale*, a scale of the specific gravity of liquids.

$$\text{Degrees Baumé} = \frac{144.3 \ (\text{S.G.} - 1)}{\text{S.G.}}$$

$$\text{Specific Gravity} = \frac{144.3}{144.3 - \text{Degrees Baumé}}$$

Hydrometers are available which read in specific gravity or degrees Baumé. If you can get those crankcase drainings cheap enough and in enough quantity, it's the way to go.

Storage

With oil, one of your costs and problems is the need for a storage tank from which to draw the oil to the burner.

You can get into a hassle here if you are not careful, and you should check out the underwriters and various local codes governing the storage of oil. In most cases they require the tank to be buried. The old system of a tank on legs is taboo today unless you are hiding in the woods. You must have a pump to supply the oil at pressure to the burner where the combustion air from the blower will do the actual atomization or vaporization; 20 to 25 pounds per square inch pressure is ample. A gear pump driven by a ¼ horsepower motor will do the trick (Fig. 4-1).

If you can get away with an elevated oil-storage tank, the pump will be gravity-fed (Fig. 4-2). If you must bury your tank, you must be sure your pump will have the capacity to lift the oil.

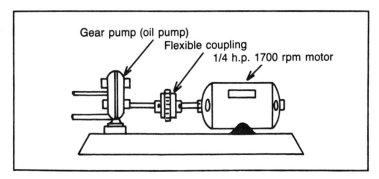

Fig. 4-1. The oil pump setup.

In the elevated tank arrangement, the added pressure to the pump is supplied by the 10 feet of hydrostatic pressure. Get this tank up high enough, and you don't need a pump at all.

If you put up a tank 50 to 100 feet in the air, however, I'm sure someone is going to notice. Underground oil storage and supply is the best arrangement and also the most expensive. The general physical arrangement is shown in Fig. 4-3.

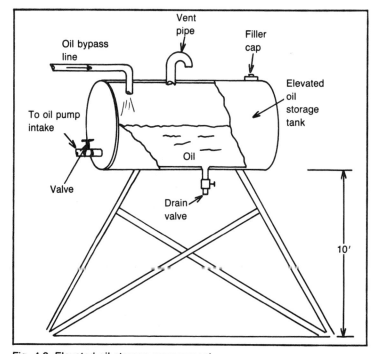

Fig. 4-2. Elevated oil storage arrangement.

Tank Size. Tanks are available in all sizes and all materials, including steel, fiberglass, and plastic. The size of oil tank is important. Unlike natural gas, where you simply turn the valve when you need it, and the meter records what you have used, you must purchase the oil ahead of time. If you run out in the middle of a heat, you are down.

Piping. You simply don't run the suction end of your pump to the oil supply and the discharge end of your pump to the burner. You must have a bypass line so you can bypass some, none, or all of the coil from the pump discharge back to the oil storage tank at will.

Figure 4-4 shows two values, A and B, and the pump and needle valve. Now, if you had only valve A, when you shut down the oil to the burner with this valve, the pump which is running would run up against a dead head. Several things could happen. The feed pipe or valve could burst; the pump could burst; you could burn up the pump motor by overloading it, or you could do all of these things.

Because the oil pump is running all the time when you are in operation, whether or not the burner is operating, the oil, if not needed at the burner, is bypassed back to the tank by opening valve B. Also, even if valve A is open, and valve B is closed, you can get a wide range of adjustment of the oil to the burner by using valve B to bypass any portion of the oil back to the tank.

Starting Up The Oil Burner

■ Refer to Fig. 4-4. To start up, first the needle valve is closed fully, then opened about ½ of a turn. Second, valve A is closed. Valve B is then opened fully, and the pump is started. Never start the oil pump unless valve B is open, and never close valve A while the pump is running without simultaneously opening valve B. This is very important and a two-handed operation.

■ Now, with the pump running, valve A closed, and valve B wide open, the oil is circulating form the oil tank through the pump up to the burner valve A and returning to the oil tank.

■ Now place a piece of burlap that has been soaked in fuel oil between the crucible and the furnace wall about 8 inches in front of the burner. See Fig. 4-5. An ignition torch can be made by wrapping burlap around a piece of 1/2-inch re-rod and tying it to the rod with bailing or soft iron wire (Fig. 4-6).

■ Light the torch or wad with a match and allow it to burn

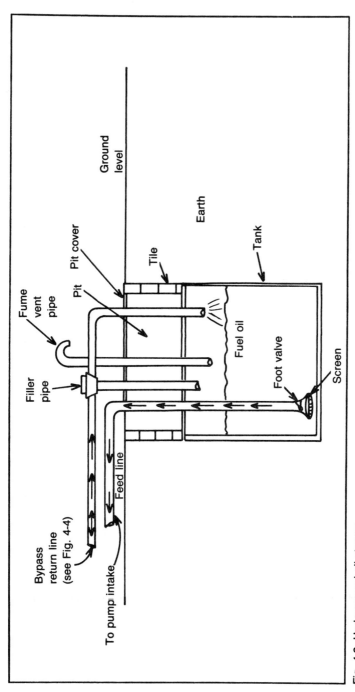

Fig. 4-3. Underground oil storage.

63

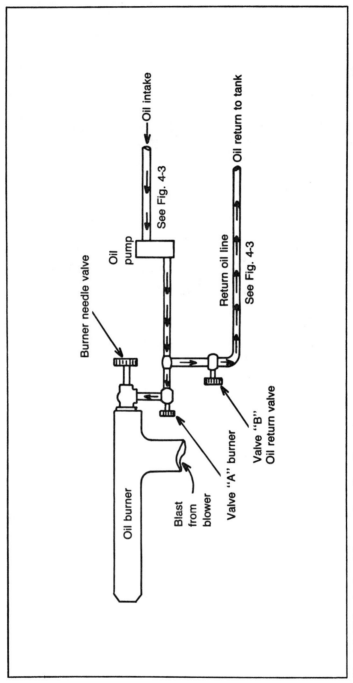

Fig. 4-4. Piping to the oil furnace from the oil supply.

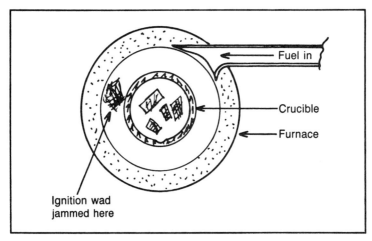

Fig. 4-5. Location of ignition wad.

vigorously. Because it is confined to a small area, you might have to use a blower to puff a little oxygen to the torch.

■ When you are certain the torch or wad is burning well, turn the air control on the blower so it is 1/8 to 1/4 open and start the blower. Now here is the tricky part. Make very sure that the torch

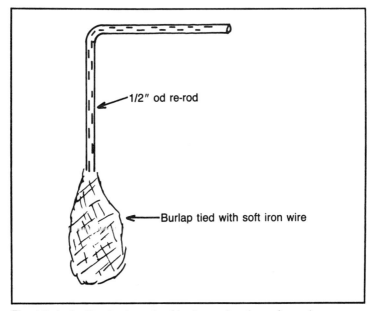

Fig. 4-6. An ignition torch made of burlap and a piece of re-rod.

or wad is burning brightly with the blower on. If the blower blows it out, shut down the blower and start over. The biggest problem is usually that the torch or wad is too small. You want a good-sized fire going here that will not be blown out by the blower.

■ When the blower is running and 1/8 to 1/4 open; the torch is burning, the oil pump is running; the needle valve is open 1/2 turn; the oil to burner valve A is closed, and the return valve B is open full, you are ready. Listen carefully and you will be able to hear the wad or torch burning with the blower running. It will make a roaring noise. If the roaring noise stops, the torch is out. Now, open valve A 1/2 turn and listen to the torch ignition. It should still be burning fiercely.

■ Now with your left hand on valve A and your right hand on valve B, start closing valve B until you hear the burner light. By working valves A and B together, you will find a point where the burner will fire nicely.

■ With the burner lit, you simply wait until the wall of the furnace is hot enough to support combustion. You then adjust valves A and B, the needle valve, and the blower to the point where you have maximum combustion. This point is always the point where the furnace makes the most noise.

■ Do not panic if you lose ignition at any point. Simply open valve B, close valve A, and let the blower clear the furnace of any unignited combustible oil/air mix. Then start over.

■ If your furnace is a box, reverberatory, or rotary furnace, or any open-flame noncrucible furnace, place an oil-soaked sack on the hearth and put an ingot or two on top to prevent it from being blown away. Don't try to light any type of furnace with crumpled paper.

You will notice in the oil tank setup that you have a foot valve on the end of the delivery pipe. This is simply a one-way flap valve that prevents the delivery pipe and the pipe to the pump from draining back into the tank and this losing the prime to the pump when the pump is not running. See Fig. 4-7.

NATURAL GAS

Natural gas is a clean, easy fuel to use. In most areas it is cheap, all things considered. Your physical hookup is simple, requiring simple, maintenance-free burners and a blower, which will operate for years with no trouble. It will not leak and produce pools of oil which can ignite. Gas rates are, as for most fuels, set on a sliding

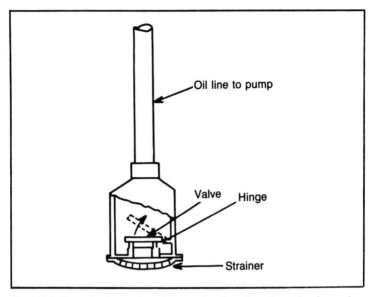

Fig. 4-7. A foot valve is used on delivery pipe from the oil supply when using an underground oil storage.

scale; the more you use, the less per therm you are paying. With a large, industrial setup, you can dicker with them on industrial rates.

The gas companies themselves are required by law to service your needs. Household pressure gas, known as *low pressure gas*, is the type of pressure you have in your home. It is expressed in inches of water; 1.73 inches of water equals 1 ounce of pressure; 27 inches equals 1 pound of pressure.

In low pressure home service, the pressure will run anywhere from 3 to 15 inches of water, but usually is somewhere between 6 and 8 inches of water, or 3.46 to 4.62 ounces of pressure. Normal gas pressure for most aluminum or brass furnaces is between 6 and 8 inches of water pressure.

If you have low pressure service, you should be in good shape. One big problem with gas, however, that is overlooked by many, is the size of the gas pipe and the distance of the run from the meter. I was called by a friend to try to determine why the small crucible furnace he built would not fire hot enough, melted at best very slowly, and never would superheat to the point he desired. He was operating on low pressure service. His shop was in back of his house about 50 feet away from the meter. The house was serviced by 1 inch line. He came off of this line with a reducing T to 1/2-inch pipe back to his furnace. The problem, as you have probably guessed, was the reduction in pipe size and the length of run.

The number of cubic feet of gas per minute (CFM) that you can deliver from a pipe is based on the input pressure, inside diameter of the pipe, and length. By the time my friend reached the furnace, the pressure at the burner was too low to give him the CFM he needed. By coming from the meter all the way back with a 1-inch pipe, the problem was solved. His reason for choosing 1/2-inch pipe was its cheapness and the ease of threading and installing.

It would take 3.7 half-inch pipes to deliver the same amount of gas as 1 one-inch pipe. A 2-inch gas pipe would deliver as much gas as 20 half-inch pipes together, or 20 times as much as 1 half-inch pipe.

As far as the simplicity of burner construction is concerned, a very simple choice is a premix burner. In this arrangement, a burner pipe is attached to the outlet of the blower, the pipe consists of only a piece of black iron pipe about 18 inches long. The gas is simply brought into the blower case or at the center of the blower intake. The gas is fed into the running blower where it is premixed with the air and delivered to the furnace ready for ignition and combustion. See Fig. 4-8. The blower output can be controlled by an intake damper, which restricts the intake opening, or by a rheostat, which controls the motor speed (Fig. 4-9).

Don't use a home shop vacuum and bring the gas into the vacuum intake. If you do, the motor in the interior of the vacuum unit, which would be in this case filled with a combustible gas/air mixture, will supply ignition in the form of brush sparking and will set off a bomb of considerable size.

SOLID FUEL

Coal, coke, or charcoal as fuels in natural-draft or forced-draft furnaces occupy only a minor position in foundries today. There is nothing wrong with their use, however. A friend of mine melts aluminum in a bucket lined with refractory. He uses charcoal briquettes as fuel and a single tuyere through which he blows with a hair dryer. He makes beautiful castings. So if you want, you can go with solid fuel.

A local high school that has a small art foundry melts both aluminum and red brass in a homemade natural-draft furnace, simp-

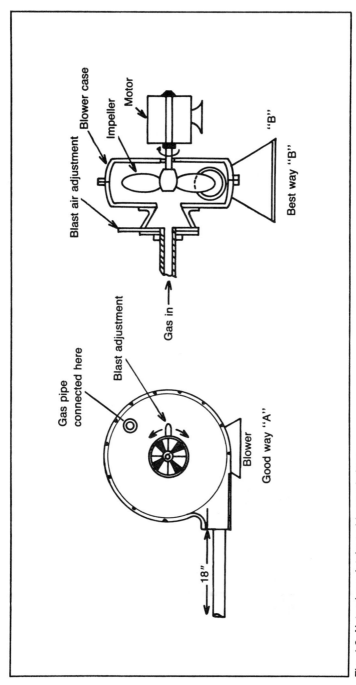

Fig. 4-8. Natural gas intake to blower choices.

69

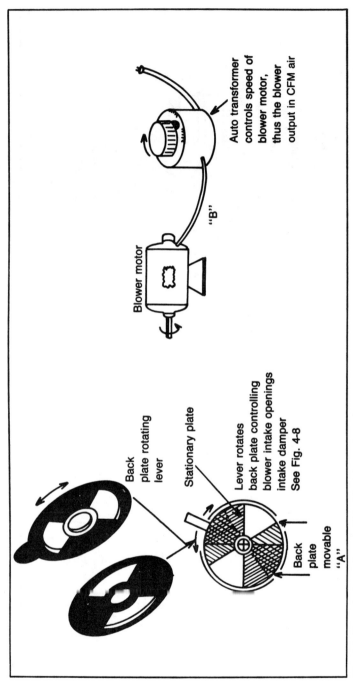

Back plate rotating lever

Stationary plate

Lever rotates back plate controlling blower intake openings intake damper See Fig. 4-8

Back plate movable "A"

Blower motor

"B"

Auto transformer controls speed of blower motor, thus the blower output in CFM air

Fig. 4-9. Two choices of controlling blast for a natural-gas premix burner.

ly because they wish to do the entire process as near as possible to the old, low-technological method used years ago.

The best solid fuel is beehive coke. It will melt more metal per pound than coal or by-product coke. The problem is getting it. To conserve coke, some operators will use hard coal under the crucible and coke for the side fire (Fig. 4-10).

Forced-draft solid-fuel furnaces melt metal much faster than natural draft furnaces and have better fuel efficiency (Fig. 3-19). It might take you anywhere from 2 to 4 times as long to melt by natural draft than forced draft, all other things being equal, because, in order to get the most BTUs from the coke you must burn it all to carbon dioxide. One pound of carbon reduced to carbon dioxide produces approximately 14,500 BTUs, but if you only burn it to carbon monoxide, you will net only 4,400 BTUs, with a net loss of 10,100 BTUs per pound of carbon. With a blower, you can easily supply the coke with sufficient oxygen to convert all the carbon to carbon monoxide then carbon dioxide in the confines and short distance the blast must travel through fuel.

I have been asked many times if it is possible to build a square furnace similar to a barbecue pit and fire it with coke, charcoal, or coal. Sure it is, but it will be a little less efficient and cost you about 5 pounds of fuel more per 100 pounds of metal melted than if it were round.

You can build one which is natural draft or forced draft with firebricks right on the ground. See Fig. 4-11. The draft can be controlled by a brick which you slide back and forth at the opening

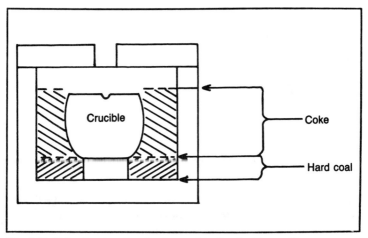

Fig. 4-10. Using hard-coal-and-coke combination fuel for melting.

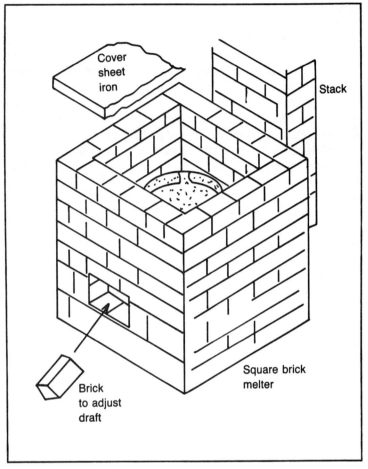

Fig. 4-11. Square crucible furnace made of firebrick.

into the ash pit. If you wish, you can simply set a blower in front of the ash pit's door for forced draft (Fig. 4-12).

Another question is how much space should be allowed between the crucible and the furnace wall for the coke. Allow 3 inches for crucibles from #40 to #100; above this size allow 4 inches. The coke bed under the crucible should be from 4 to 6 inches. A common mistake is to allow too much space, thinking the more coke the better. In reducing the space between the crucible and the furnace wall from 6 or more inches to 3 inches, you will find the aluminum will melt faster; the furnace will be hotter; and you will reduce your fuel consumption by as much as half. See Fig. 4-13.

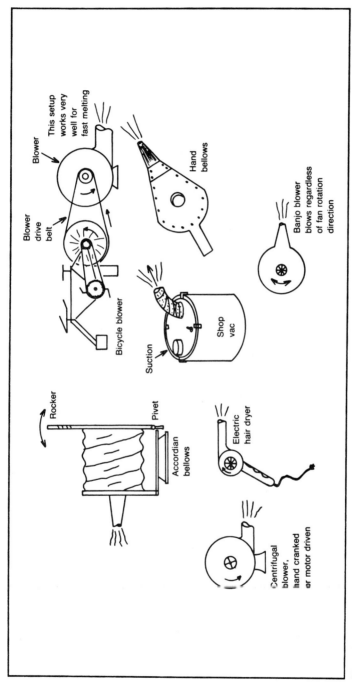

Fig. 4-12. Various ways of supplying forced draft for solid fuel melters.

73

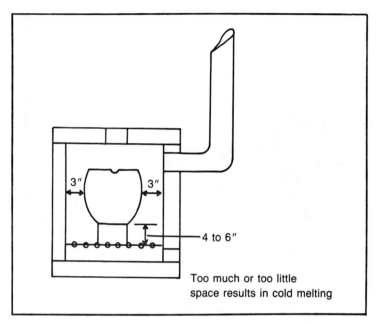

3″   3″

4 to 6″

Too much or too little
space results in cold melting

Fig. 4-13. Correct space for fuel in a coke- or charcoal-filled crucible or an ironpot melter.

BLOWER SIZE

I have talked about oil, natural gas, and solid fuel as fuels, but you can also consider oxygen as a sort of fuel. It takes oxygen for the air to support the combustion and burn the carbon of the fuel to CO then CO_2. The reaction of this process produces heat, which is needed to reduce the solid metal to a liquid.

The amount of air required for the combustion of any fuel can be approximated easily by dividing the BTUs of the fuel by 100. Thus, if we have fuel oil that has a value of 145,000 BTUs per gallon:

$145,000 \div 100 = 1450$ cubic feet of air needed to burn the oil.

For natural gas, at 1000 BTUs per cubic foot:

$1000 \div 100 = 10$ cubic feet of air per cubic foot of gas. Coal rated at 13,000 BTUs per pound would require 130 cubic feet of air per pound.

Unless oil is reduced to a vapor, it cannot be ignited, similar

74

to the gasoline in your car. The oil is atomized by pumping the liquid under pressure through a fine orifice controlled by a needle valve. This produces a fine spray of atomized oil (the finer the better). The air for combustion from the blower surrounds each minute oil globule, vaporizing it to produce a combustible mixture. The finer the particles of oil, the greater the surface area per unit, and the warmer the oil and air blast, the more efficient and hotter the flame will be. When the air is heated prior to mixing with the fuel, it is called *hot blast melting*.

The usual type of oil burner for crucible furnaces is the low-pressure, air atomization type. See Fig. 4-14. The fuel is brought up to the burner at 20 to 25 pounds of pressure by a simple gear pump. The air is supplied at 16 ounces of pressure, figuring 1350 to 1500 cubic feet of free air per gallon of fuel; 60 percent is required for atomization.

In choosing a blower size, you can use Table 4-1, which shows the approximate fuel consumption of #3 fuel oil per hour or 1000 BTUs per cubic foot natural gas. The blower required is calculated as follows.

If it takes 1450 to 1500 cubic feet of air to burn 1 gallon of 145,000 BTUs oil, and a number 30 crucible burns 1.2 gallon of oil per hour, you will need a blower that will deliver at least 1.2 × 1500 cubic feet of free air. If you are burning 1000 BTUs gas, and the approximate consumption of natural gas per hour for your #30 crucible furnace is 170 cubic feet, you will need 10 cubic feet of free air for each cubic foot per hour, or 1700 cubic feet.

All these figures can be confusing. You have the difference between high vs. low heat input to your furnace. The object to get as many BTUs into the furnace in as short a time as possible. If you increase the heat input, you decease the time it takes to melt and superheat, and you use less fuel in the process. This is why

Table 4-1. Choosing a Blower Size.

Size of Crucible		Burns:
30 = 1.2	Gal. oil per hr.	or 170 cu. ft. per hour gas
40 = 1.7	" "	or 214 cu. ft. per hour gas
50 = 1.85	" "	or 243 cu. ft. per hour gas
60 = 2.25	" "	or 290 cu. ft. per hour gas
70 = 2.8	" "	or 316 cu. ft. per hour gas
80 = 3.	" "	or 358 cu. ft. per hour gas
90 = 3.	" "	or 382 cu. ft. per hour gas
100 = S3.5	" "	or 390 cu. ft. per hour gas

some furnaces take as much as twice the time as others to melt a given amount of metal.

You will find that there are a lot of small crucible furnaces on the market that have a short blower CFM capacity. Let's take an example. I purchased a small-crucible, gas-fired furnace to melt silver. The furnace took a #6 crucible, which gave me a capacity of about 15 pounds of silver per melt. With the freight plus 3 crucibles, it came to about $500. The blower was a very small squirrel cage, the kind you buy for about $10.00, complete with motor. With the blower going full bore, I could only open the gas line about half way for maximum combustion. It took from a cold start about 1½ hours to melt 15 pounds of sterling silver and superheat it to 2100 degrees Fahrenheit. After two heats, I gave up and bought a big enough blower and increased my burner size from 3/4 inch to 1 3/4 inches. The heat from a cold start to 2100 degrees Fahrenheit took only 36 minutes, and with a hot furnace each heat after that took 18 minutes.

The point is, put your money into your blower and burner. You are much better off to have a blower 20 or 30 percent larger than needed then not have enough CFMs. Blowers are rated in cubic feet per minute (CFM) at a given revolutions per minute (RPM) at so many ounces of pressure. The factors involved are the displacement of air it will discharge in cubic feet per minute, the RPM that you turn the blower, and the horsepower of the driving motor. The horsepower required is dependent upon the static pressure.

Static pressure is the resistance offered by the area in the furnace against the air being blown in by the blower. If the blower is underpowered so that it cannot overcome this resistance but simply loads up the motor, slowing it down then slows the volume of air delivered because of less RPM.

For example, a #2 Buffalo blower at 4,320 RPM will deliver 247 cubic feet of air per minute against 3 ounces of pressure · ' en driven by 0.53 horsepower. The same blower at 5,595 RPM will deliver 310 cubic feet of air against 5 ounces of pressure when driven by 1 horsepower.

For a furnace, you must have a pressure blower. A squirrel-cage blower will not do the trick. It is designed to move a volume of air against none or very little static pressure. If you get a blower that will deliver 500 CFM at 4 ounces of pressure driven by a 1 horsepower motor, you can use this with a wide range of size and design of melting furnace, regardless of fuel choice.

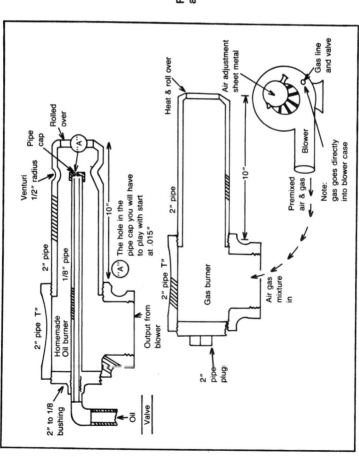

Fig. 4-14. Low pressure homemade oil burner and homemade natural gas burner.

77

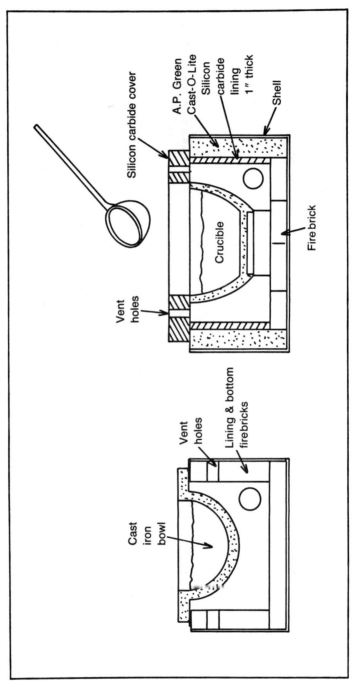

Fig. 4-15. Basic dig-out iron pot or bowl-shaped crucible.

TYPE AND SIZE OF FURNACE

The type and size of furnace depends upon what you are going to do; however, anything smaller than a #10 crucible presents a problem because the metal will cool off very fast when the furnace is shut down. With very small crucibles you must pour at once. It stands to reason that a large volume of metal will stay liquid over a much longer period of time than a small volume. Too large of a crucible used to pour molds of low pouring weight (mold cavity volume) is also a problem. The metal is generally too cold by the time the last quarter of the crucible is poured.

If you have a small jobbing foundry and are pouring lightweight castings from 1 to 15 pounds, a #60 crucible in a stationary furnace is a good bet. If more volume of metal is needed, it is sometimes much better to have several #60 furnaces, giving you continuous hot metal, rather than a large furnace. This arrangement also allows you to run just one furnace when you have a light metal demand. Melting small amounts in a large furnace is a losing proposition.

You must examine your immediate metal needs and try to project your future needs carefully. Decide on which type of furnace you should buy or build, then go at least 10 percent above this figure for a safety factor.

If you have the time, build your own furnace. It's really not that complicated, and the difference in cost between building a furnace and purchasing one is extremely wide. you can scale down or up the simple crucible furnace plans shown in Fig. 3-27. A dip-out furnace can be built using either a bowl-shaped crucible or a cast-iron pot (Fig. 4-15).

5

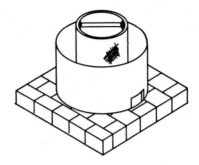

Furnace Refractories

Very little information is given in most books on foundry practice about furnace refractories in general, what type you should buy, how it should be installed, or what care is needed. There is a very wide variety of selection, and the cost can vary widely.

The word *refractory* pertains to any material that is not damaged by high temperatures. Such materials are made into bricks, used to line furnaces or, ladles, etc. The material could be anything from sand, silicon carbide, clay, carbon, or mixes of various types of material. Which material or combination you should choose depends upon the service to which it is going to be subjected, including the working temperature, furnace design, furnace atmosphere, and the chemistry of the slag if it is in contact with the refractory.

SIMPLE LINING

Let's look at the simplest and cheapest, fairly serviceable furnace lining for a lift-out crucible or dip-out furnace.

Shell Lining

■ The shell of the furnace is 12-gauge black iron riveted or welded together, with no bottom. The shell can be a garbage can, oil drum, or whatever. See Fig. 5-1.

■ Cut out an opening for the burner and a safety slag hole in case the pot breaks. See Fig. 5-2.

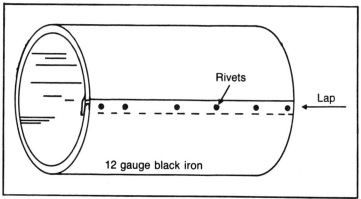

Fig. 5-1. Furnace shell.

■ Plan exactly where you want to place your furnace in the shop and lay down a firebrick base. See Fig. 5-3.

■ Now build a tapered cylindrical form to represent the inside diameter of the lined furnace.

■ Weld a piece of pipe or cold roll across the top of the big end of this inside form. See Fig. 5-4. The lining is going to be rammed between this form and the inside of the furnace shell. The bar is used to draw the form from the furnace after the lining is completed. A slight taper or draft on the form allows it to come out easily without damaging the newly rammed lining.

■ The shell is placed in position on the brick base.

■ The inside form is given a coating of cup grease, then placed, small end down, in the center. See Fig. 5-5.

■ A wood block is placed in the slag hole, and a round block

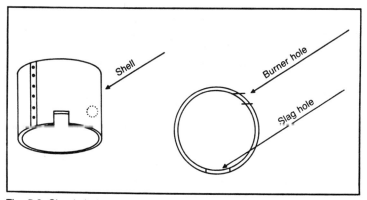

Fig. 5-2. Slag hole burner hole.

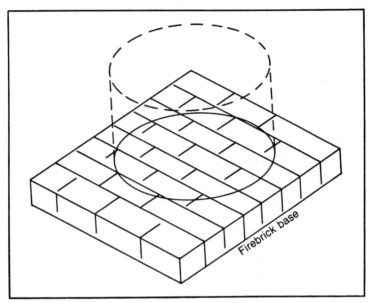

Fig. 5-3. Brick base for furnace.

is placed in the burner hole from the inside form to the outside of the shell. See Fig. 5-6. You might elect to place the two wooden plugs in place after you have rammed your lining up to the bottom side of the two shell openings (burner and slag hole).

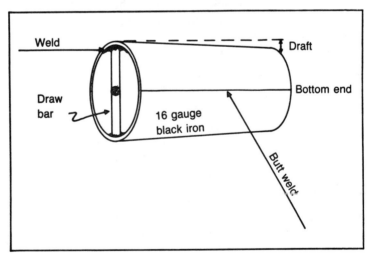

Fig. 5-4. Form used to ram lining in furnace shell and to replace lining when necessary.

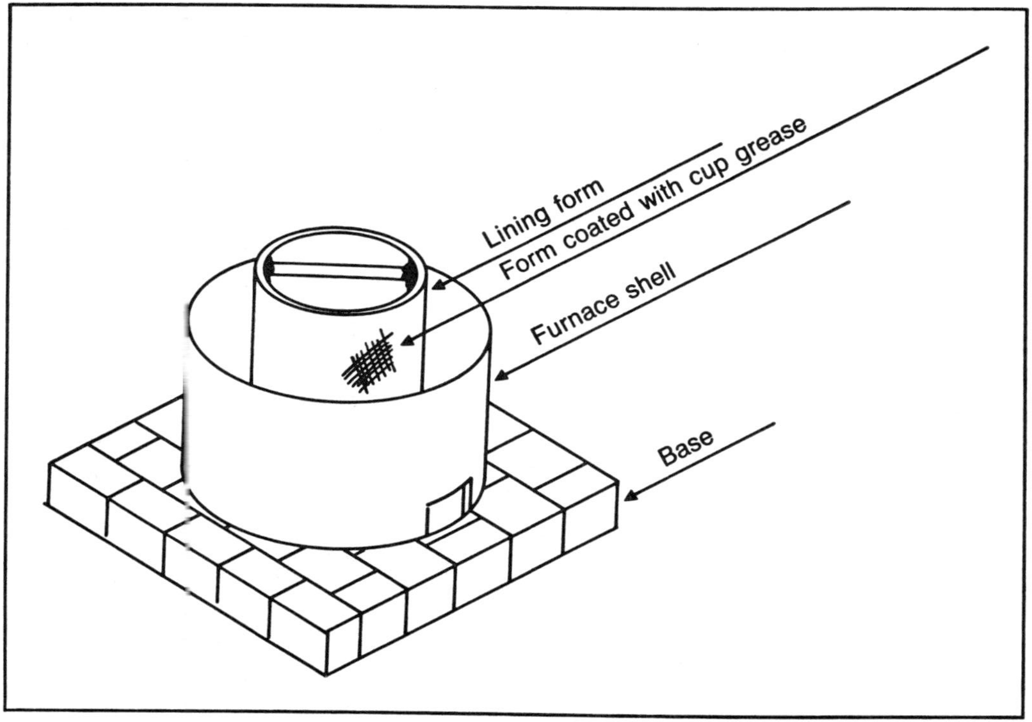

Fig. 5-5. Ramming ready to ram lining.

Lining form coated with cup greease

Form shell

Furnace shell

Base

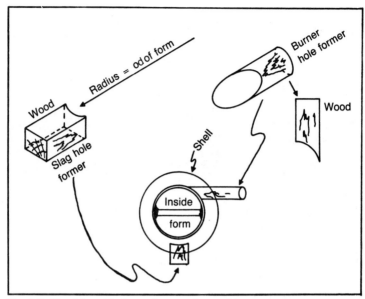

Fig. 5-6. Wood forms to form slag opening and burner port.

■ To line the furnace, use a simple lining material, such as fireclay and grog.

Fireclay is defined as clay consisting principally of aluminum oxide and silica, which will only soften at high temperatures. *Grog* is ground-up firebricks. Grog is available in various grinds, from very coarse to powder.

■ Of course, you can make your own for a clay/grog lining. You want the grog to be about 50 percent pea sized and 50 percent walnut sized. The mix is by volume three parts grog and two parts fireclay. Mix the dry ingredients thoroughly and add just enough water, about 6 percent, to get the consistency of a real dry cement mix. When mixing, add a little water at a time, mix well, then add a little more water, until you have a mix that is wet but not mud and has no dry spots.

■ Because the grog is bone-dry and porous, it helps to soak the grog in water until it stops bubbling. Pour off the water, then add the dry fireclay and proceed as just discussed. The mix should be just wet enough so that you can mold it into a ball with your hands, and it will hold together, yet not be sloppy or dry and crumbly (about like modeling clay).

■ Now place a layer of your mix between the shell and inside form about 3 inches deep. With a chunk of 2 × 4 lumber, work

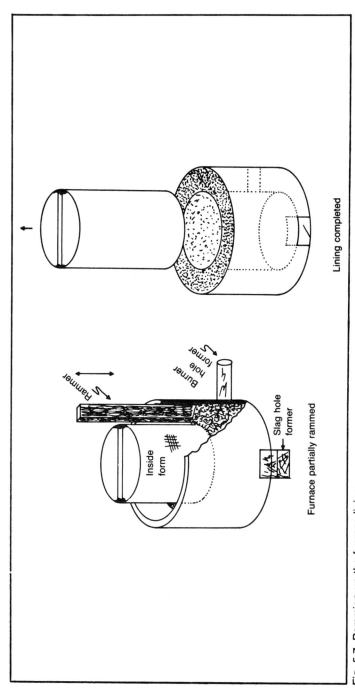

Fig. 5-7. Ramming up the furnace lining.

Inside form

Rammer

Burner hole former

Slag hole former

Furnace partially rammed

Lining completed

your way around, tamping the mix tightly in place and being careful not to shift the inside form. Once you have this first layer in tight, it will not shift. Now simply work yourself up to the top in 3-inch segments (Fig. 5-7).

■ When you have finished lining the shell, trowel the top off flush. Rap the inside form with a soft mallet to shake it loose and pull it out. Finish the burner hole and slag hole. See Fig. 5-8.

Cover Lining

The cover is rammed into a tapered steel ring with a form to make a center hole 6 to 7 inches in diameter. See Fig. 5-9.

■ To ram the cover, place some newspaper down on a flat cement slab. Let the lining and cover air-dry for a day or two.

■ Build a wood fire inside the shell with the cover on, but propped up with a few pieces of firebrick. See Fig. 5-10.

■ Let the fire burn down and then rebuild it. Repeat this process several times. Remember the more moisture you put into your original mix, the more it will shrink during drying, and the tougher it will be to get it dry.

■ The final curing is done with the burner. A 4-inch molding sand bottom is rammed into place around your pedestal block. See Fig. 5-11.

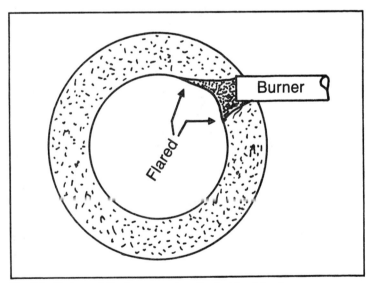

Fig. 5-8. Flaring out the burner port on the inside of the furnace.

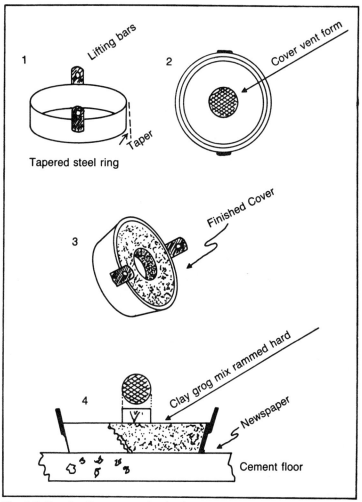

Fig. 5-9. Constructing a cover for the furnace.

■ Build a new wood fire inside and replace the cover propped up. Now with the burner in place, light the furnace with the burner, firing as low as possible. Let it run until the lining quits steaming. See Fig. 5-12.

The use of a molding sand bottom might strike you as strange; however, this type of a bottom is very efficient. It is also a real lifesaver when you have an accident in the furnace, such as a busted crucible or slag buildup. It's easy and cheap to remove, replace, and maintain.

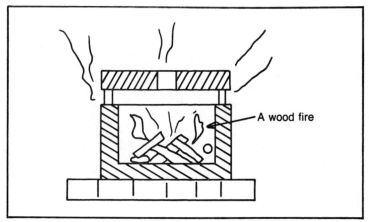
Fig. 5-10. Drying the lining and cover with a wood fire.

■ When the lining quits steaming, start working the burner up a notch at a time until you are firing the maximum BTUs that the burner will put out at this point. Run the furnace for at least 1 1/2 hours to set up the lining, or vitrify it.

The result is a monolithic firebrick lining. If you would have taken the mix of fireclay, grog, and water and made a brick and then fired it in a kiln, you would have the same product. The mix is what is called plastic firebrick. More on this later.

Carborundum

Carborundum makes very fine, long-lasting, strong furnace linings, covers, and pedestal blocks. For a homemade lining mix, use 80 parts by volume of carborundum 60 mesh with 20 parts by volume of fireclay.

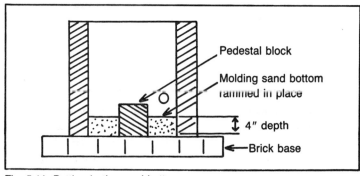

Pedestal block

Molding sand bottom rammed in place

4″ depth

Brick base

Fig. 5-11. Putting in the sand bottom.

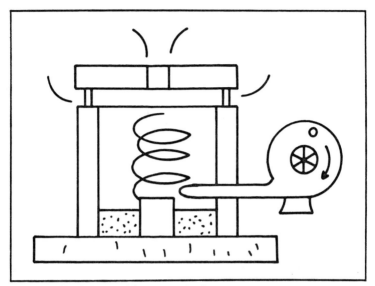

Fig. 5-12. Final drying of furnace under fire.

Mix well together and then temper like molding sand with a 50/50 mixture by volume of water and silicate of soda. Ram it into place the same way you did with the plastic fireclay. The silicate of soda holds it together until you fire the lining up to a vitrification point. This mix is also used to repair linings, ladles, lips, etc.

Another patch mix which works well is: fireclay 4 1/2 parts by volume, manganese oxide 1 1/2 parts by volume, borax 1/2 part by volume, and salt 1/2 part by volume. Add just enough water to form a thick paste.

Silicon Carbide Linings

Silicon carbide is a hard, black, insoluble substance with a melting point of 2700 degrees Centigrade or 4892 degrees Fahrenheit. This material is widely used as the innermost surface of the furnace lining.

Because silicon carbide is expensive and has such a high thermal conductivity, it must be insulated from the furnace shell in order for you to be able to take advantage of its properties. There are a number of materials which can be used to insulate it, including castable linings, firebricks, and plastic firebrick. See Fig. 5-13.

Because of its high thermal conductivity, it will radiate the heat back to the crucible. In doing so, it will cut the melting time by at least 15 percent, as well as cut fuel cost by a sizable amount.

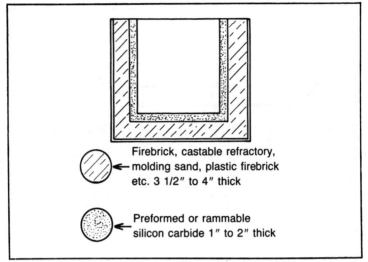

Fig. 5-13. Silicon carbide rammed inner lining.

It also has an excellent resistance to thermal shock, abrasion, and erosion.

This material is also available as preformed inner linings or as a rammable cement. See Fig. 5-14. Even if your furnace lining is firebrick or one of the castable or rammed linings without a silicon carbide inner lining, a very good practice is to use silicon carbide cement to patch your lining, and as a wash applied to the lining on regular intervals.

Crucibles made of silicon carbide are also available. They are long-lasting but much more expensive than clay graphite crucibles.

FURNACE COVERS

The cover should be 3, 3 1/2, or 4 inches thick, depending upon the furnace size. The exhaust hole should be 8 inches in diameter for covers 28 inches and larger, and 6 to 8 inches for covers smaller in diameter. The bearing surface should be at least 3 inches on the furnace. See Fig. 5-15.

BASE BLOCK

The base block, or *pedestal*, should be made of the same material as the crucible and the same diameter as the crucible bottom. Hold the crucible to where the junction of the base block and crucible are on the center line of the burner port. See Fig. 5-16.

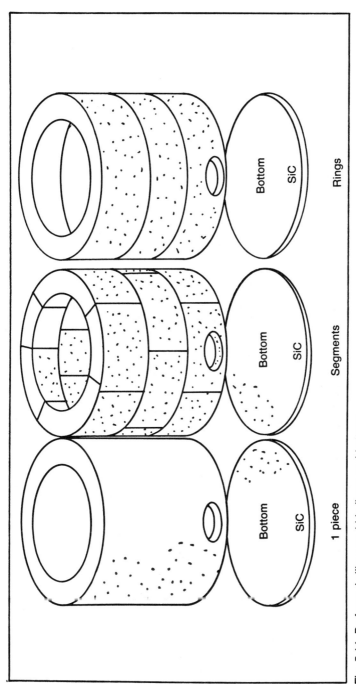

Fig. 5-14. Preformed silicon carbide liners and bottoms.

1 piece   Segments   Rings

Bottom SiC   Bottom SiC   Bottom SiC

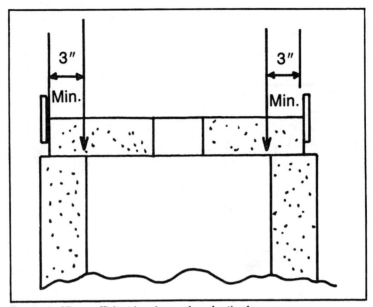

Fig. 5-15. Allow sufficient bearing surface for the furnace cover.

FURNACE CONSTRUCTION MISTAKES

Some common mistakes made in furnace construction follow:

■ The lining is too thin.
■ The shell is too thin.
■ The cover is too thin.
■ The vent hole is too small or too large. The size of the vent hole is extremely important to the furnace operation.

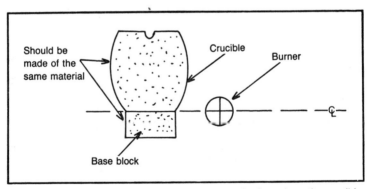

Fig. 5-16. The centerline of the burner must be on the line where the crucible and base block meet.

■ The cover is too close to the crucible. You must allow 2 to 3 inches.

■ There is inadequate combustion space in the furnace. If you do not have sufficient space in the furnace for the fuel mixture to combust and expand, the result will be a great loss of uncombusted fuel out of the cover vent. In extreme cases, the furnace will fire outside rather than inside the furnace.

You need approximately 1 cubic foot of combustion space for each 40,000 to 60,000 BTUs released per hour at a furnace operating temperature of 2000 to 2500 degrees Fahrenheit, and 1 square inch of vent area for each 20,000 to 25,000 BTUs liberated in the furnace per hour. For example, if the furnace fuel consumption is 100 cubic feet of natural gas per hour with a BTU value of 1000 BTUs per cubic foot, you have 1 million BTUs. Divide this by 20,000 BTUs and you come up with a vent area of 50 square inches, or an 8-inch hole, which has an area of 50.265 square inches.

■ There is insufficient blower capacity.

■ The gas line is too small in diameter, and/or the run from the meter is too long.

■ There is no seal where the burner pipe comes into the furnace. See Fig. 5-17. If there is a leak where the burner pipe comes into the furnace, secondary air will be drawn in, making it next to impossible to adjust for the correct mixture of fuel to air.

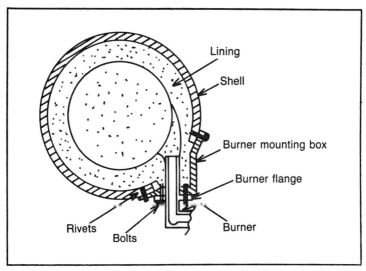

Fig. 5-17. Best construction of burner attachment to the furnace for a tight fit and good seal.

93

BRICKS, CASTABLES, AND RAMMING REFRACTORIES

There is no end to the types and kinds of refractories available from the various refractory companies. Firebricks, shapes, castables, and plastic refractories can be purchased for any particular service, temperature, slags, mechanical abuse, etc.

For a melting furnace for aluminum, I am very much in favor of the castable or plastic refractories, where you can produce a monolithic lining and cover much easier then with fired preshapes such as firebricks.

I do not want to endorse A.P. Green Refractories company nor to infer that their products are superior. I do, however, wish to call out some of their castables and plastics which have given me excellent results over the years.

A.P. Green Super Plastic is a superheavy-duty plastic refractory used in high temperature zones where the temperature of operation is up to 2910 degrees Fahrenheit. It is excellent material for monolithic furnace linings, bottoms, and covers, and as a ladle liner.

A.P. Green Red "X" is a very good material for use on thin linings rammed against an insulating material, brick, or castable. See Fig. 5-18. This is also a good rammable ladle liner or patching material.

A.P. Green has various other plastic refractories. They all come in 100 pound cartons and are damp ready to use.

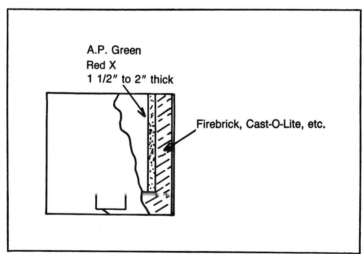

A.P. Green
Red X
1 1/2" to 2" thick

Firebrick, Cast-O-Lite, etc.

Fig. 5-18. A.P. Green's Red X makes a good, cheap inner lining rammed over almost anything.

94

A.P. Green castables come as a dry mix with a binder. You simply add the amount of moisture needed, mix the material like cement, and cast it in the desired shape. They are hydraulic-setting; no heat is required to develop strength; less heat is lost through the furnace walls, and they are easy to install. A.P. Green has a complete line of castables to meet the requirements of every type of service up to 3400 degrees Fahrenheit.

A.P. Green MC-22 is a favorite of mine for furnace linings and covers up to 2350 degrees Fahrenheit. It is great for small or large aluminum furnaces, is strong and tough, and comes in 100 pound containers. You need 128 pounds for each cubic foot.

Super Kast set is another good product for uses up to 2800 degrees Fahrenheit.

Kast-O-Lite is a great castable with great insulating properties; although it is not as tough as MC-22 or Kast set from the mechanical standpoint. It takes the place of insulating block or brick. The best way is to cast the lining with Kast-O-Lite and then ram a 1-inch inner lining of Red "X." It is a lighter material than MC-22 or Super Kast set, and only 83 pounds are needed per cubic foot.

I built a #60 crucible, stationary aluminum furnace out of all Kast-O-Lite with no inner lining, and I used this furnace daily for both brass and aluminum melting for 7 years before I had to replace the lining. Although the top end temperature recommended by A.P. Green is only 2500 degrees Fahrenheit, I experienced little wear and tear even with some occasional high-nickel heat, where the metal superheat temperature exceeded 2500 degrees Fahrenheit.

6

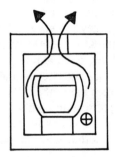

Melting and Fluxing Aluminum

I have talked about various furnace construction, refractories, etc. I believe it is very important to first build or purchase a good melting unit. Only then can you successfully melt aluminum. Once you have a good furnace, you can get to the business of the proper melting practice. An improperly designed furnace will not only drive you crazy but have adverse affects on the quality of your melt. Before I discuss the melting process, however, I should first say something about crucibles.

CRUCIBLES

The history of crucibles stretches back some 3000 years before Christ. Ancient metal workers found they could smelt the metals from their ores in a hole dug into a bed of clay, with the aid of forced air from a mouth blowpipe and charcoal as a fuel. When the art of pottery was developed, the idea of using clay pots, or *crucibles*, was the next step. It was then easy to handle the metal, and the fuel could be placed around the crucible for better heat transfer, etc.

Crucibles from the ancient times contain carbon in the clay structure. The carbon found is thought to have come from particles of leaves, roots, and other vegetable matter which was converted into carbon during the firing of the pots by the potter. The local founder of ancient times probably made his own crucibles or had the local potter do it for him. The first crucible business, to my knowledge, was recorded early in the 16th century in Bavaria. Early in the 18th century, crucible makers added natural graphite to their clay mixes to produce a more stable and refractory product with a longer life.

The first real change from the clay-graphite crucible was the development of the carbon-bonded silicon carbide crucible during the first World War. The formulas and manufacturing processes of crucible makers are, as it must have been in the beginning, closely guarded secrets.

Composition Groupings

Carbon-bonded crucibles are crucibles with a high percentage of silicon carbide and graphite and lesser amounts of other refractories, such as clay. The bond is formed from the residual carbon resulting from the distillation of such organic material as tar and resins. The major proportion of the crucible is refractory components. The internal and external surface of carbon-bonded crucibles are usually glazed with a protective coating to prevent the crucible proper from oxidizing.

Clay-bonded crucibles are made of a high percentage of graphite as well as a percentage of silicon carbide. The bond is inorganic ceramic consisting of various clays. These crucibles are often called *ceramic-graphite*.

Oxide crucibles are made of a foundation of various oxides such as alumina, magnesia, silica, zircon, and mullite, as well as various clays. The major application is in high-temperature work, ferrous melting, chemical work, and such. Some are rated for use at temperatures as high as 5000 degrees Fahrenheit. They are usually straight-sided for electric-induction tilt furnaces. For the aluminum foundry, the old clay graphite crucible or melting bowl is very satisfactory.

Care

Crucibles are costly, and in order to get the maximum safe life out of them, you must apply certain rules as to their care and use. Because a crucible is actually a ceramic pot, it must be handled carefully, as you would any ceramic item.

■ When you receive a new crucible, inspect it for obvious flaws. Tap the crucible with a light rawhide mallet, not too hard (Fig. 6-1). It should ring with a clear note, like a bell. If you get a dull thud, there is a flaw somewhere, such as a crack or internal

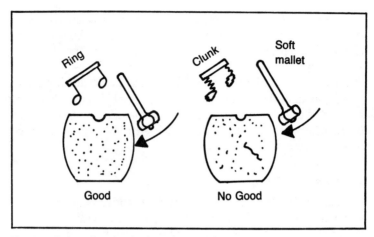

Fig. 6-1. Soft mallet check of a new crucible.

bubble. Send this crucible back to your supplier for a replacement.

■ Always store your crucibles in a warm dry area; behind or beside the core oven is a good place. If you put a wet crucible in a furnace and fire it up, it simply explodes.

■ If the crucible is too large to carry in your arms, don't roll it on its side or on the bottom edge, carry it with come-out tongs or on a dolly. See Fig. 6-2.

■ Use the correct height and diameter base block for the crucible. See Fig. 6-3.

■ Charge a crucible very carefully so you do not damage it. If ingots are wedged, when they expand they will burst the crucible. Dropping a heavy ingot or chunk into the crucible can damage it; so ease the charge in with tongs. See Fig. 6-4.

■ Always melt with a slightly oxidizing flame for minimum gas absorption by the melt and for a longer crucible life. You can purchase an instrument called an *Orsat* to check the flue gas for the percentage of carbon monoxide and carbon dioxide, or adjust the furnace to the point where the combustion makes the maximum amount of noise. At this point, you should be about neutral, neither oxidizing nor reducing.

If a flame is oxidizing, it has more oxygen than is needed to combust the fuel. If it is reducing, then you have an insufficient amount of oxygen to combust the fuel.

■ Now, when the furnace is making the maximum noise (when you are melting red brass or any copper alloy), you simply increase the air to the blower until the burned gasses coming out of the vent

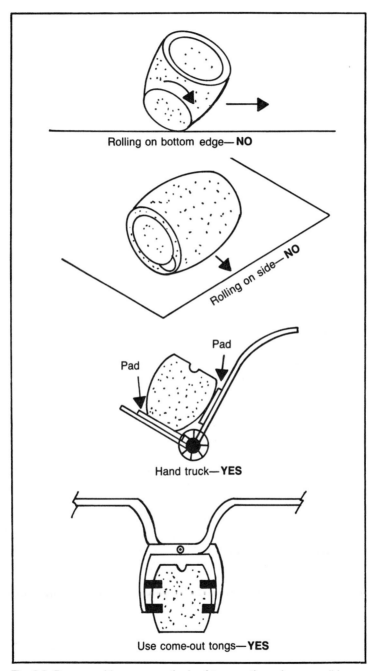

Rolling on bottom edge—**NO**

Rolling on side—**NO**

Pad

Pad

Hand truck—**YES**

Use come-out tongs—**YES**

Fig. 6-2. Proper and improper methods of transporting a large crucible.

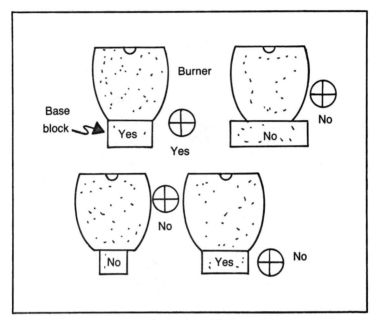

Fig. 6-3. Correct height and size for base blocks.

in the cover show a tinge of green on the outside of the flame. At this point oxidizing conditions prevail. A smoky red or yellow flame coming from the cover vent indicates that conditions are highly reducing.

In some cases with a copper-aluminum alloy, you can see a slight green tinge at oxidizing conditions. A very easy way to tell is to hold a piece of clean, cool, polished, pure zinc in the flame coming from the cover vent for a few seconds. If the zinc turns black, or slightly yellow the burner is adjusted to reducing. Increase the air to the burner until the zinc test shows no change in color; at this point the conditions are oxidizing.

▧ Always place the crucible exactly in the center of the furnace, with a piece of corrugated cardboard between the bottom of the crucible and the pedestal block. The cardboard prevents the crucible from fusing to the pedestal block, a process which can damage the crucible bottom when it is removed from the furnace.

If the furnace is hot, simply soak the cardboard in water, then place it on the pedestal block, and quickly place the crucible on it. When the crucible is in the center of the furnace, it is heated evenly and not stressed. See Fig. 6-5.

▧ New clay-bonded crucibles should be brought up to

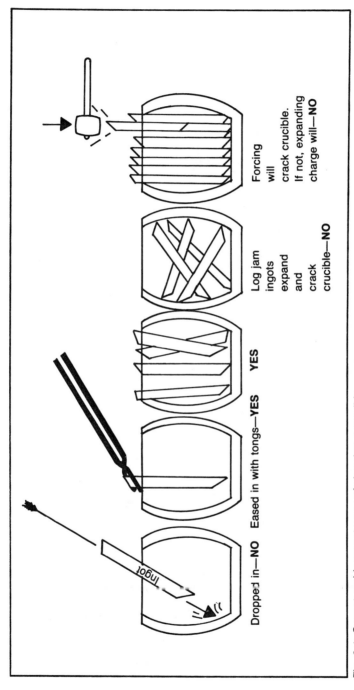

Dropped in—**NO**   Eased in with tongs—**YES**   **YES**   Log jam ingots expand and crack crucible—**NO**   Forcing will crack crucible. If not, expanding charge will—**NO**

Fig. 6-4. Correct and incorrect ways of charging a crucible.

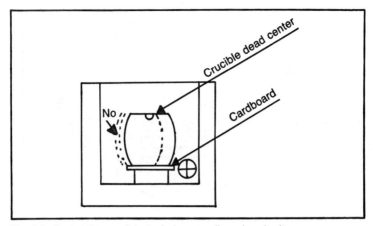

Fig. 6-5. Center the crucible and place cardboard under it.

temperature slowly the first time they are used to ensure proper annealing and the safe removal of any contained moisture. New carbon-bonded crucibles should be brought up to melting temperature as rapidly as possible so the proper function of its protective glaze is ensured.

■ Crucible handling hardware, such as lifting tongs and pouring shanks, should fit properly. See Fig. 6-6.

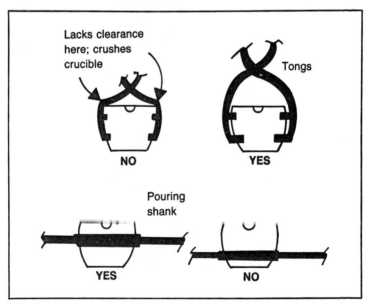

Fig. 6-6. Proper fit for crucible-handling hardware is essential.

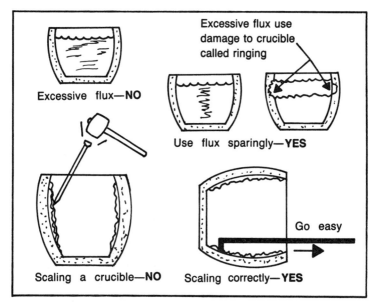

Fig. 6-7. Proper fluxing and cleaning of a crucible.

■ Use none or as little flux as possible. Also, the correct flux is very important. Some fluxes will eat up a crucible in no time. For aluminum, use a little borax if you like. See Fig. 6-7.

■ Cleaning a crucible to remove dross and metal oxide buildup should be done very carefully. Do not use excessive force, such as a chisel and hammer, to dislodge the buildup. An automobile spring leaf bent at right angles and ground on an arc does a very good job. Scrape gently with this tool while the crucible is hot. See Fig. 6-8.

MELTING

There has been a ton of material written about melting aluminum, and all sorts of fluxes and treatments have been recommended. Some are beneficial, and some are extremely harmful.

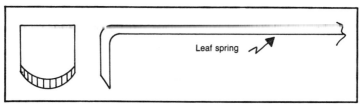

Fig. 6-8. Proper design of a crucible scaling tool.

Looking at the problems involved is the key to understanding how best to melt. If you were to ask the average foundry supply company what you needed in the way of fluxes, degassers, etc., for melting aluminum, you can bet that he will come up with a rather large selection of snake oils and secret powders that are absolutely necessary.

One such item has been around for years by many suppliers; it is in the form of a doughnut which slips over a rod with a flange. This doughnut is a cure-all, and when you read the advertisement, you wonder how you ever got along without it. You simply slip one or more of them on your application tool and plunge it to the bottom of the molten aluminum, and your troubles are over. See Fig. 6-9.

If you quiz the supplier as to just what is the compound in the doughnut, you will be informed it is an ancient formula handed down by the ancient pharoahs of Egypt. They come in red, green, and blue. What is it? Well it is one of several well-known chemical compounds alone or in combination, zinc chloride, aluminum chloride, sodium chloride, or potassium chloride. Most, but not all, fluxes, etc., are needed only to correct poor foundry practice in the first place, however.

Although aluminum is among the easiest metals to cast, you can get into all sorts of problems. It requires a lot more know-how than it appears on the surface. Before you pour your first pound of molten aluminum, you must carefully study and understand every

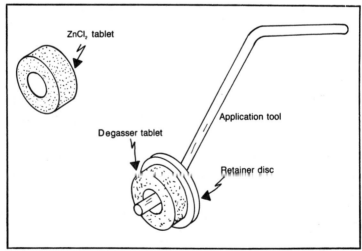

Fig. 6-9. Degasser tablets and application tool.

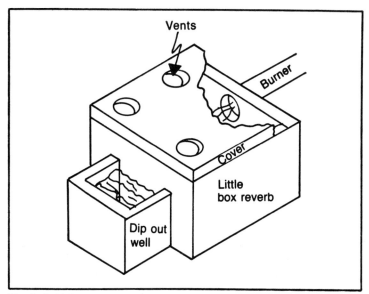

Fig. 6-10. Little box dip-out furnace.

process up to and including the pouring of the aluminum into the mold. You cannot produce a good aluminum casting with gassy, dirty, oxidized, contaminated melt. If you intend to melt several different alloys, use a stationary left-out crucible furnace with a crucible for each alloy to prevent cross-alloy contamination. If you melt basically one type of alloy, you might choose to melt in a dip-out, stationary, crucible furnace, a cast-iron crucible pot furnace, or a little box dip-out reverberatory. See Fig. 6-10.

Cast-Iron Pots

Cast-iron pots are great, and the fuel consumption is less than crucible furnaces because the cast iron has a much higher specific thermal conductivity. They melt fast, which is good; however, you have the problem of iron pickup, requiring a wash coating to protect the melting aluminum from contacting the iron pot. This coating must be applied frequently. Because you must clean the pot down to the bare metal prior to each wash application, it could become a hassle. You can also have iron contamination from local wash failures.

Various types of washes are available to the trade, or you can make a mix of chalk and water glass, fireclay and water glass, or graphite and water glass. Paint it on when the pot is just warm to the touch, then let it dry from the residual heat before firing the pot up to temperature. Another problem with cast-iron pots is the formation of sludge in the bottom of the pot. This sludge is usually found as a sandy semiliquid on the bottom of the pot. In severe cases, it has formed up as a hard, brittle, crystalline solid. The composition consists of aluminum-iron-manganese complex, aluminum-chromium-silicon, and aluminum-iron-silicon intermetallic compounds. It is a precipitation eutectic problem when a piece of solid aluminum scrap or ingot is charged to the molten aluminum in the cast-iron pot. It sinks to the bottom and chills that portion of the melt.

The solid chunk then slows melts and tends to leave behind the compound with the higher melting points. If you keep adding solid chunks to the melt to maintain a volume of metal in the pot, this reaction occurs repeatedly, and results in a buildup of these sludges in the bottom of the pot. This problem is found where you are pouring continuously, say into a permold, and when you keep adding solid metal to the pot. If you simply melt down a cast-iron pot full of aluminum, and then dip out to pour sand molds until the pot is empty, never adding new stock, you will not have much of a problem. If you wish a continuous supply of metal in your iron pot, melt aluminum in a ceramic crucible and pour it into your iron crucible.

Self Healing

There is a tendency to fiddle with the melt—stir, agitate, and add various fluxes and treatments—and this is where most of your problems start. Don't monkey with the melt. Most aluminum heats require no flux of any kind.

If you charge clean sprues, ingots, or scrap, simply melt it down, skim off the dross (which would be very little), and pour. If left alone and undisturbed, this dross, or skin, forms the best protection for the melt against further oxidation. If you break this film, the clean, exposed surface will immediately form a new oxide skin, thus healing itself. You can continue stirring the pot of molten aluminum until you have nothing but a pot of aluminum oxide. Leave it alone.

It pays great dividends to keep your metal supply clean, dry, and stored in a clean area. Scrap auto pistons are a favorite supply of many small shops. They must be free from rings, wrist pins, retainers, grease, and carbon. Very often it pays to sandblast your dirty scrap prior to using it. Avoid extremely finely divided scrap

106

and turnings. If you generate a lot of turnings in your operation, the natural tendency is to melt them; however, it is usually wiser to sell them off as scrap or swap for heavy cast scrap. Unless you have a way to remove the cutting fluids, dirt, etc., and a way to duck these turnings under a large heat of molten metal or make them into as dense a briquette as possible, your melt loss due to oxidation will be terrific. Unlike red brass oxides, you cannot reduce the aluminum oxides back to liquid aluminum. Once they are oxidized, there is no recovery.

FLUXING

Fluxing, if you must, is considered as a supplement to good melting practice, and should not be a substitute for it. Some fluxes are designed to remove hydrogen absorption, and some are designed to separate metal from oxide films and dross at the melt's surface (drying fluxes). It's quite common to have a dross on the melt consisting of 10 percent aluminum oxide and 90 percent liquid aluminum.

The purpose of the drying flux is to separate the oxides from the liquid aluminum, allowing the aluminum to drop into the molten aluminum below it and leave only a dry dusty aluminum dross (oxide) to be removed from the surface of the melt prior to pouring. A dross rich in aluminum can result in a considerable melt loss. It is quite common to see a pile of skimmings with liquid aluminum running out beneath it. Your skimming should be nothing more than a dry, gray-whitish, light powdery oxide easily removed with the skimmer. See Fig. 6-11.

Some fluxes are formulated to remove absorbed hydrogen from the melt and also milk the dross free from unoxidized liquid aluminum. These fluxes accomplish both purposes only to some degree. It is much better to go after the dross with one treatment and the gas in the melt with another.

Chlorine As a Flux

Volatile chloride salts have been used for years for fluxing aluminum. They include zinc chloride, aluminum chloride, sodium chloride, and potassium chloride. When these salts are heated, they break down and release chlorine gas.

Chlorine is a greenish-yellow gas with a pungent, irritating odor. It is extremely toxic by inhalation, with a tolerance of only one part per million in air. It is extremely irritating to the eyes, respiratory

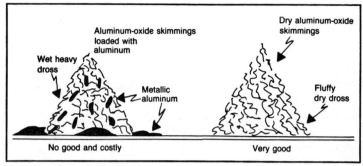

Fig. 6-11. Wet and dry dross.

system, and skin. In the process of removing hydrogen from the aluminum, the chlorine is released from flux as a gas. This gas combines with the hydrogen absorbed by the aluminum melt to form another toxic gas, hydrogen chloride, which bubbles up and out of the molten aluminum. Hydrogen chloride is soluble in water to form hydrochloric acid. If you breathe this gas, you wind up with a respiratory system full of hydrochloric acid, extremely corrosive acid. The tolerance of hydrogen chloride in air is set at five parts per million. In addition to these problems, hydrogen chloride will react violently with aluminum; so these chloride fluxes are hazardous to use.

If you use a zinc chloride flux, you have the problem of the reaction of the zinc chloride with the melt. The zinc is imparted to the melt, and if the alloy being melted has a specification calling for a low zinc tolerance, this addition of metallic zinc could exceed the limit.

Fluorine

Fluorine can also be used; however this presents a real health hazard. Fluorine as potassium flouride is toxic by ingestion and skin contact, with a tolerance of only 2.5 milligrams per cubic meter of air. The fluorine atom has a valence of -1; therefore it will combine with a great host of things. In fact it forms compounds with most elements except helium, neon, and argon. Using it as a flux in the gaseous state as fluorine, or as a fluoride, it is soluble in water to form an aqueous solution known as hydrofluoric acid. This is an extremely dangerous and corrosive acid which will actually dissolve glass. It is also highly toxic. If it comes in contact with the eyes, fluorine gas will in most cases cause instant and permanent blindness.

HYDROGEN

A major problem with melting aluminum is its ability to absorb hydrogen from the products of combustion, from wet metal in the charge, from the moisture in the atmosphere, from molding sand, damp flux, damp skimmers, improperly or incompletely dried ladles, furnace linings, or even improperly designed gating systems which allow moist air to be sucked in with the stream of molten metal entering the mold. This problem is called *hydrogen occlusion*. Certain materials have the property of *absorbing*, or occluding, some gasses, by the formation of either a chemical compound or a solid solution.

With aluminum you only have to worry about hydrogen absorption. Oxygen will form with molten aluminum to make a protective coat, or dross, on top of the melt, and if this is left alone, no further oxidation will take place. Now, because hydrogen is readily soluble in molten aluminum, but largely insoluble in solid aluminum, the hydrogen is dissolved in the molten metal. When the aluminum solidifies, the dissolved hydrogen is rejected from the aluminum as a gas, and more or less of this gas trapped in the solid as porosity. The aluminum gets its hydrogen from the high reactivity of aluminum with oxygen. It robs the moisture of its oxygen to form aluminum oxide and *nascent hydrogen* (hydrogen that is set free in a chemical reaction).

Nascent hydrogen is more active than hydrogen in its ordinary state, probably because hydrogen in the nascent state is in single atoms rather than molecules. Therefore, ordinary gaseous hydrogen is not significantly soluble in aluminum, but in the nascent state, it is a bad actor. Hydrogen solubility in aluminum is low at the melting point of aluminum, but at 1500 degrees Fahrenheit it is impossible to avoid gassing of the heat.

To lessen this reaction whereby nascent hydrogen is produced, you must operate your fuel-fired gas or oil furnace in a slightly oxidizing state, that is with the burner operating with a slight excess of air. By doing so, you maintain your protective cover of aluminum oxide and minimize the reaction with the oxygen or water vapor.

If you operate with a reducing atmosphere, the hydrogen absorption will jump in leaps and bounds. In a crucible furnace, if the cover of the furnace is too close to the crucible, you will get a rippling effect of the melt surface as the exhaust leaves the vent hole and will increase the hydrogen pick up. See Fig. 6-12.

So, as outlined, the rules are simple: Melt slightly oxidizing;

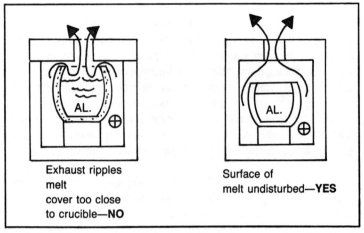

Exhaust ripples
melt
cover too close
to crucible—**NO**

Surface of
melt undisturbed—**YES**

Fig. 6-12. Sufficient clearance between the furnace cover and crucible should be allowed to prevent rippling of the metal surface which would result in excessive oxidation and gas absorption.

don't overheat the melt; don't hold the melt; pour when the melt is ready; melt only dry stock; use dry tools; use dry flux; avoid agitation of the metal at all times—during melting, transferring the metal, and pouring—pour close to the sprue.

Gas and Shrinkage

I made the statement that at 1500 degrees Fahrenheit you are going to get some hydrogen absorption no matter how careful you might be. Is some gas porosity O.K.? It all depends on the quality of the casting being produced. The most common rule is that some gas and normal shrinkage are fine for the average casting. The most common test is to pour in green sand or a core mold a sample, or *test cock,* 2 inches in diameter and 2 inches tall. See Fig. 6-13.

You simply pour a cock from a small hand ladle and watch it solidify. From this you can get a fairly good idea of how much gas content you are up against. Watch the shrinkage the cock takes. See Fig. 6-14.

Now look at the results of the test cocks in Fig. 6-14. "A" is so gassed that a casting poured from the melt will look like swiss cheese. "B" would also be useless to pour. "C" is less gassy and might be suitable for the casting and its end use. D is much less gassy, and "E" might be so free of gas that it presents a problem with risering and gating due to excessive shrinkage. Actually castings made from the melt that produced a shrinkage as shown

110

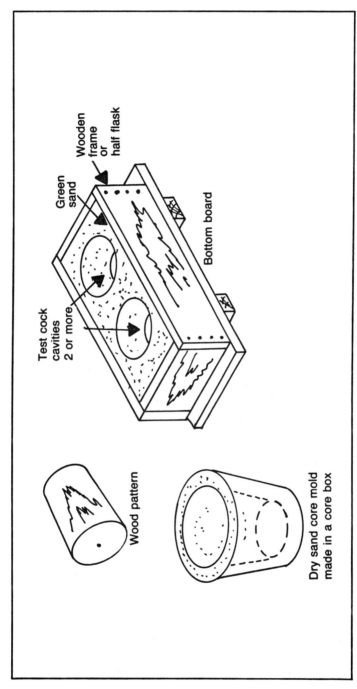

Fig. 6-13. Molds to pour shrink test cocks dry sand and green sand.

Wooden frame or half flask

Green sand

Test cock cavities 2 or more

Bottom board

Wood pattern

Dry sand core mold made in a core box

111

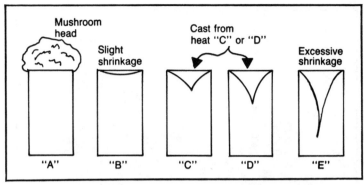

Fig. 6-14. Test cocks indicating the gas absorption.

in D would, although containing some gas porosity, be satisfactory for most work.

Very little is ever said about the positive effects of some gas porosity. Normal shrinkage for most aluminum alloys is around 5 percent. This is quite a bit and is the reason for the risers and chills. Small amounts of gas in the melt produce a microscopic porosity throughout the casting. A finely grained casting may have as much as 2 percent of this microscopic porosity. You can't see it, but it is very beneficial because it can reduce the apparent shrinkage to as low as 2.5 to 3 percent. This reduction in shrinkage results in a very substantial reduction in the number and size of the feed risers required, and in some cases it eliminates the riser requirement on small and medium castings of good design with even walls.

A problem which comes up often is when a casting being made continually with good results out of the blue starts to develop shrinkage porosity, starts to leak under pressure, and requires larger risers to correct. The problem occurs because the melt is being degassed extensively.

Let's look at this problem. We have a casting which is to be pressure-tested and must work under pressure from water, gas, etc. This casting is poured with a heat that does not have most of the hydrogen removed. On solidification, the hydrogen in the melt has manifested itself as porosity throughout the casting. See Fig. 0-15.

A sample casting is checked under pressure, and it is pressure-tight. A sample is sectioned and examined under the microscope only to find that it contains considerable gas porosity. The next melt is then completely degassed and a sample poured. This sample is free from hydrogen gas porosity but leaks like a sieve under

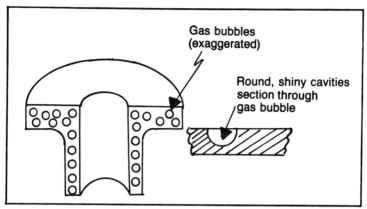

Fig. 6-15. Gas porosity in a casting.

pressure. A sample is sectioned and examined, and shrinkage porosity is found (Fig. 6-16).

Why does the casting with as porosity not fail (leak) under pressure, and the casting with shrinkage porosity leak like a sieve? The answer is that *gas porosity* consists of individual bubbles which are not connected together, and *shrinkage porosity* is not bubbles, but a discontinuous porous structure caused by voids between the *dentrites*, or crystal growth, which lacked sufficient feed metal to fill in as the crystals formed during solidification. These voids are connected together, leaving a path to the outside of the casting. See Fig. 6-17.

The only salvation of a leaky casting is to increase the feed metal via risers, chills, or hydrostatic pressure (more sprue and riser

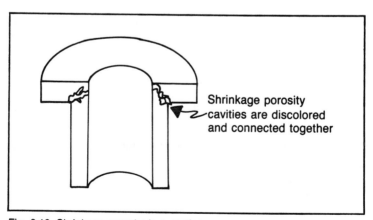

Fig. 6-16. Shrinkage porosity in a casting.

113

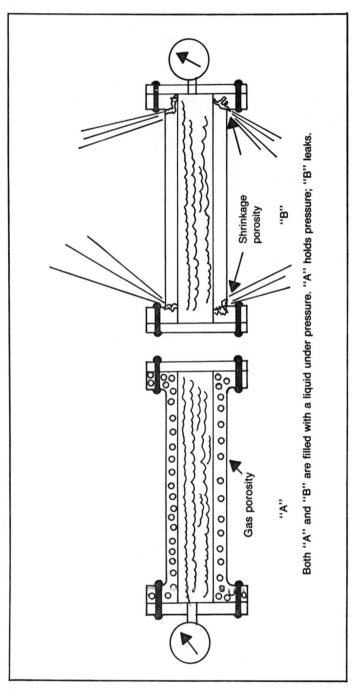

Shrinkage porosity

"B"

Gas porosity

"A"

Both "A" and "B" are filled with a liquid under pressure. "A" holds pressure; "B" leaks.

Fig. 6-17. Effect of gas porosity vs. shrinkage porosity under pressure.

height) or by the introduction of some hydrogen into the melt, such as for permanent-mold piston castings.

There is a limit to the amount of gas porosity that can be tolerated, however; and excessive gas porosity can lead to a much too coarse structure of grain. In castings that are subject to X-ray, polishing, plating, and anodizing, the gas porosity is disclosed and will lead to rejection. It's a paradox. Porosity reduces tensile strength and elongation; however, pinhole porosity has little effect on pressure tightness, yield strength, fatigue strength, or the endurance of limited commercial aluminum castings.

Vacuum Testing Equipment

Vacuum testing equipment will allow you to check the metal of the furnace and actually will accentuate the presence of hydrogen, showing it in amounts below atmospheric pressure. You can build this equipment, and it will save you countless castings. The equipment consists of a vacuum pump, a pressure cooker, a motor, and a coupon mold.

Parts. From Fig. 6-18 you will see that there are three major pieces—a standard, family-size pressure cooker, a small vacuum pump capable of producing 15 to 20 inches of vacuum, and a suitable motor. Several pumps are available, complete with motor. Pump and motor are mounted on a base with enough room for the pressure cooker. The stem on the lid of the cooker that carried the check valve is replaced with a short nipple, a tee, a nipple, and a gas cock, as per the drawing. If it is desired, a gauge can be installed in the place where the little metal safety valve is located. At any rate, this little metal valve is removed; if no gauge is used, it is stopped off, or the gas cock is put there, deleting the tee. With this done, a length of strong rubber hose, such as that used on blowpipes, is attached between the pump and the lid of the pressure cooker. Make sure that the hose is attached to the suction side of the pump and that the pump rotation is correct.

Procedure. Place the preheated coupon mold in the pressure cooker and start the pump. The lid should be off, with the relief cock open. With a hand ladle, pour a sample from your degassed heat into the coupon mold in the pressure cooker. Quickly lock the lid on and close the relief cock. Allow the coupon to solidify in the vacuum chamber about 1½ to 2 minutes. A little fiddling soon will give you the correct timing. Release the vacuum by opening the gas cock, remove the lid, take out the coupon mold, and knock out the coupon into a bucket of water. Now section it with a hack or

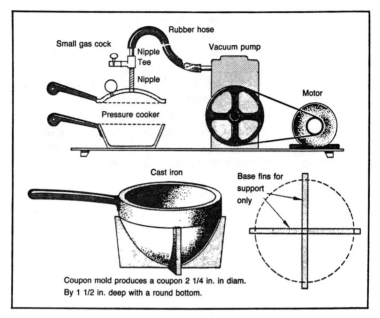

Fig. 6-18. Homemade vacuum-testing equipment for hydrogen.

band saw and file smooth one of the surfaces with a vixen file. If the heat still is gassed, porosity will be clearly visible to the naked eye. Degas until a clean vacuum sample is produced.

You will find that this system of vacuum testing will show even very small traces of gas. These coupons make excellent samples for etching and for micrographs. I know of two large producers of quality aluminum castings who have used this system for a number of years with excellent results. They check every heat by this method.

Under a vacuum, the hydrogen in the test sample expands to a huge size; so don't be alarmed. See Fig. 6-19.

Dry Nitrogen

Your simplest and best bet for removing dissolved hydrogen from a melt is dry nitrogen. Nitrogen is a colorless, odorless, and tasteless gas and is nontoxic. Nitrogen, if bubbled up through liquid aluminum, will remove the dissolved hydrogen. Exactly how it does so is a little vague; it is believed that the action is mechanical rather than a chemical reaction. The physical removal of hydrogen is believed to be caused by the migration of the hydrogen into the low-pressure nitrogen bubbles as they rise to the top of the molten

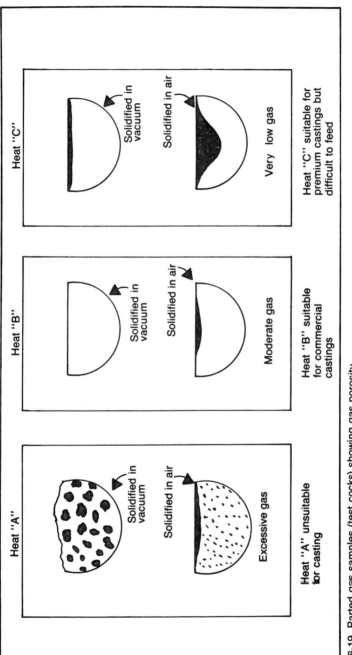

Fig. 6-19. Parted gas samples (test cocks) showing gas porosity.

aluminum, a kind of a hitchhike affair. Dry nitrogen is fairly cheap and can be purchased from any local welding gas supplier. The setup is simple. See Fig. 6-20.

The regulator should be equipped with a flow meter in liters or cubic feet per minute in order for you to determine how many cubic feet of nitrogen you have bubbled through the melt in a given time. The nitrogen is turned on, the tube inserted into the crucible to the bottom, and the regulatory delivery pressure adjusted to give you a nice even flow of nitrogen without agitating the surface of the melt beyond a gentle movement. The delivery pipe, if made of black iron, should be coated on its outside surface with a good refractory wash and be well dried. A refractory clay tube or graphite tube would be a better bet. About 4 to 6 cubic feet of nitrogen per 100 pounds of molten aluminum should do the trick. After the treatment, allow the melt to settle 10 to 20 minutes, then skim and pour.

A superior procedure is to use a mixture of 90 volumes of nitrogen to 10 volumes of chlorine or 80 volumes of nitrogen to 20 volumes of chlorine. These two gasses are mixed through flow meters. See Fig. 6-21. Sample the heat via a poured test cock or vacuum tester and then determine if it needs to be degassed.

Hexachloroethane supplied as a dry powder wrapped in aluminum foil or in compressed tablets can also be used as a source of chlorine to degas the heat. This type of flux is submerged to the bottom of the melt with a tool you can make. The tool is called

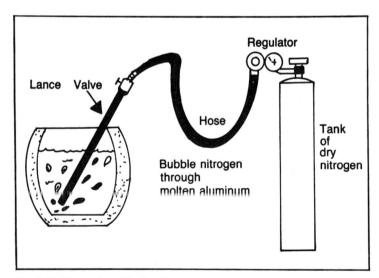

Fig. 6-20. Degassing with dry nitrogen.

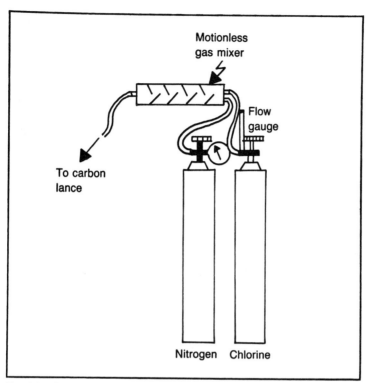

Fig. 6-21. Degassing with mixed gasses of dry nitrogen and chlorine.

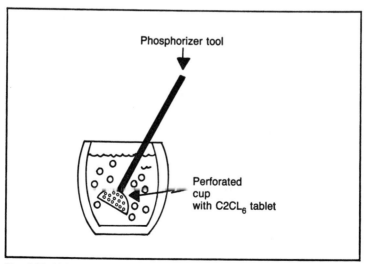

Fig. 6-22. Using a phosphorizer tool to degas aluminum.

a *phosphorizer* because it is used to dunk phosphorus deoxidizers in red metal heats. See Fig. 6-22.

The tool consists of a steel half-round perforated cup attached to a suitable cold roll rod terminating in a handle. The flux is thrown on to the metal and then quickly dunked to the bottom. The heat releases the chlorine from the flux. The chlorine bubbles up through the perforations in the cup and through the liquid aluminum.

Whenever you are fluxing or skimming, make sure that whatever tool you use is bone dry. A good hood over your furnace with a forced draft is a must when degassing, especially with chlorine-producing chemicals.

7

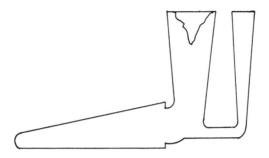

Aluminum Foundry Practices

As I stated, aluminum is relatively easy to cast, and you have quite a choice of casting methods—sand, investment, plaster of paris molds, metal molds, carbon molds, and die cast (pressure or gravity). The ease comes from its light weight, low pouring temperature, and high fluidity at its pouring temperature.

SAND CASTING

Because aluminum melts at such a relatively low temperature, and because it is lightweight, there is a very broad range of natural or synthetic sands with which you can work. The sand need not be near as refractory as you would require for brass, iron, or steel; nor do you require high-density molds with a lot of hot and dry strength, because it has only a light weight to be supported by the mold cavity. You can use an extremely fine sand to produce exceptionally smooth castings. The typical properties of a natural bonded sand for a wide range of aluminum casting weights are as follows: permeability, 5; green strength, 7 to 8; clay content, 15 to 20; grain fineness, 265.

Aluminum sand molds are rammed or squeezed much lighter than other metals because of the light mold pressure. Simply ram the mold up just firm enough to support the weight of the aluminum and the hydrostatic pressure. A mold hardness of 50 to 60 is usually as high as you need to go, compared to 70 or 90 for brass or iron. You actually cannot tell anything about mold hardness with your thumb, except for mush soft and rock hard.

CASTING TOOLS

There are several tools a caster should own to produce problem-free castings. They include a mold hardness gauge, a venting wire, and a whistler.

Mold Hardness Gauge

It pays great dividends to own a mold hardness gauge (Fig. 7-1). The gauge will not only tell you the mold hardness but will, by taking various readings over the cavity, show you how evenly the mold is rammed. A mold rammed very unevenly with some sections too soft and others too hard will not produce good castings. You can have swells, blows, and gas-porosity defects all the same casting.

The mold hardness gauge is very expensive; however, the advantages of having one greatly offset the cost. If you lose one medium or large casting because of too soft or too hard of a mold, you have spent the cost of a mold hardness gauge, and they last a lifetime.

The operation of the gauge is simple; you press the gauge down on the sand until it is in flat contact with the face of the anvil. As the half-round button is spring loaded, it will penetrate the sand more or less, depending upon the hardness of the sand. The dial indicator will show the mold hardness (Fig. 7-2).

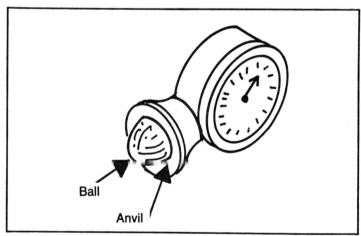

Fig. 7-1. The mold-hardness gauge.

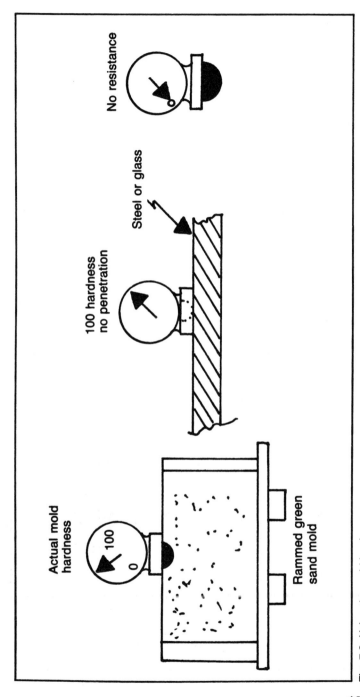

Fig. 7-2. Using the mold-hardness gauge.

123

Vent Wire

The most important tool of the molder, but very often an overlooked one is the lowly vent wire. The time spent with the vent wire is well spent, and regardless of how minor the operation of venting seems, it is more often than not the difference between a good casting and a lost casting. Also, you are only talking about a minute or less per mold. Make yourself a vent wire and use it both on the drag and the cope. Ram the drag vent, ram the cope and vent, and draw the pattern. See Fig. 7-3.

The Whistler

Another very often needed, but seldom used, device is the whistler. This tool serves a multiple purpose. The whistler is usually made with a shellacked, 1/4-inch diameter wood dowel with a small brad point to keep it from moving during ramming. You can try to push a whistler through the cope after the cope is lifted and the pattern is drawn. Place your hand on top of the mold sand where you want the whistler to come through, and push it through from the inside of the cavity. If, however, you should hit an obstruction in the rammed sand, such as a rock, piece of tramp metal, paper, etc., you could wind up pushing a big chunk of the cope out. See Fig. 7-4.

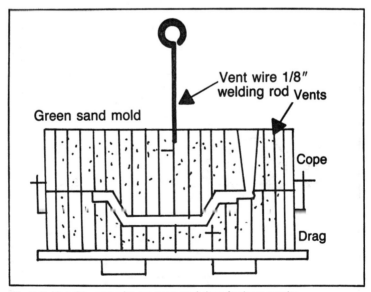

Fig. 7-3. Use the vent wire on cope and drag for best results.

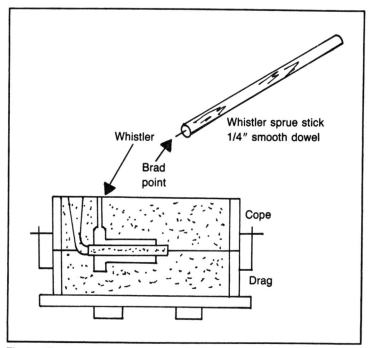

Fig. 7-4. The whistler indicates when the mold is full and also relieves back pressure.

The whistler is placed on a high point, usually far from the gate, and in some cases you might elect to put more than one whistler on the casting. The whistler allows the air in the mold cavity to be expelled very rapidly from the mold during pouring, thus reducing the back pressure against the oncoming metal flow. The pressure reduction is considerable compared to the channel the mold cavity air must escape through (i.e., the rammed sand or, the cope/drag joint). It cuts down considerably on the time required to fill the mold and is often the deciding factor in running a thin section. It also allows you to see when the mold is full, resulting in much less overfills and runoffs at the pouring basin. See Fig. 7-5.

Unlike the vent wire, the whistler can, if not properly used, act like an ineffective riser and produce a defect in the casting. If the whistler solidifies too fast, it can pull feed metal from the area of attachment, causing a shrink defect at this point. Because the key to good gating is dependent upon directional solidification toward the gating system and risers, you must keep this in mind when you use whistlers. See Fig. 7-6. Make sure that you fillet the

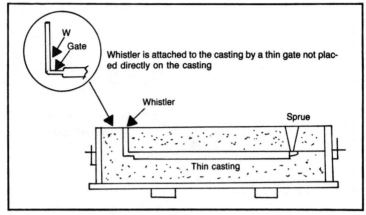

W
Gate

Whistler is attached to the casting by a thin gate not placed directly on the casting

Whistler

Sprue

Thin casting

Fig. 7-5. Use the whistler to assist in fast mold filling of a thin cavity.

junction of the whistler with the casting. See Fig. 7-7.

The displacement of the body of air in the mold cavity presents no problem with a casting with large feed risers. See Fig. 7-8.

FOUNDRY PRACTICE PROBLEMS

Now it's not all duck soup with aluminum molding sands. Two

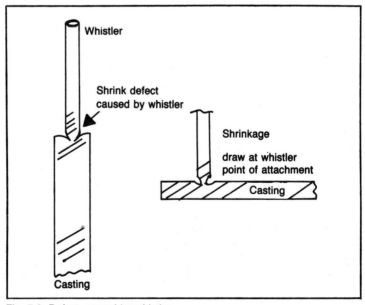

Whistler

Shrink defect caused by whistler

Shrinkage

draw at whistler point of attachment

Casting

Casting

Fig. 7-6. Defect caused by whistler.

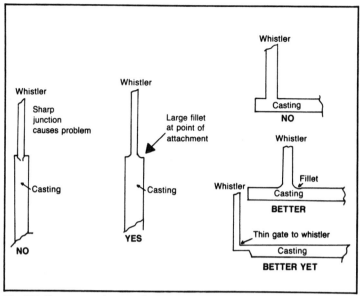

Fig. 7-7. Proper attachment of whistler.

things will have to be carefully considered and controlled: permeability and moisture content.

When you are casting a metal with as low a density as aluminum, it is harder for the alloys to rid itself of oxides or to drive off mold gasses. The heavier or more dense a metal, the less problem. Therefore, in order to come up with good oxide-free castings

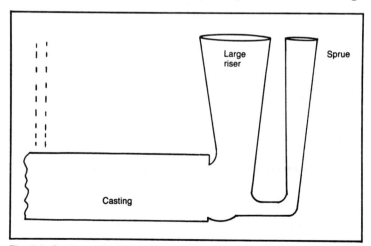

Fig. 7-8. Castings with large risers have no need for a whistler.

127

which do not have blows or hydrogen porosity, you are going to need sufficient permability, whereby the cavity can be filled quietly and quickly with a minimum of back pressure. The air and water vapor must have a free path to escape through the mold walls and core vents to the outside. Any gas, vapor, or air pressure generated during the pouring of a mold is going to take the path of least resistance. If the mold does not have sufficient permeability, the path will be through and into the liquid metal in the mold. The water vapor will break down to form dissolved hydrogen in the liquid metal. We have already covered this problem. See Fig. 7-9.

What causes a gassy, blowy casting? Assuming that the metal was melted and degassed properly, and the metal is delivered to the mold in a dry ladle, the problem is caused by one or more bad practices from that point on. The cause could be inadequate fillets on the pattern; excessively thin sections of the casting, requiring too high of a pouring temperature to run them; pouring too hot; wet sand; molding sand too fine, mold rammed too hard; mold improperly vented; cores not dried properly; or too low of a base permeability of the sand.

Casting Smoothness

There is and has been way too much emphasis put on casting smoothness. Everybody seems to be trying to make glass-smooth castings, regardless of their end use. This is a big mistake if you

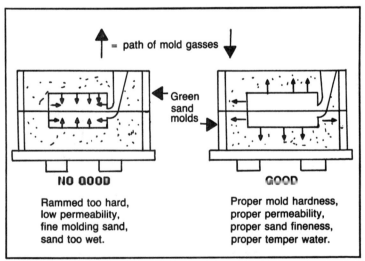

Fig. 7-9. Steam takes the path of least resistance.

128

are making a gear blank or a machine part. You should look very carefully at its end use.

I'm not talking about roughness like a corn cob, where the sand is so open and coarse that the surface is like coarse sand paper. You would be very much surprised at how smooth a surface you will get on an aluminum sand casting produced in a sharp silica sand of 100 to 120 mesh bonded with 12 percent clay. In many cases, it would be a much better practice to use a fairly open sand and to face the mold with a fine sand if you need an extremely fine, smooth surface for cosmetic reasons, such as a plaque or art piece.

You do not need a glass-smooth sash weight. If you try to make every casting as smooth as possible, regardless of its end use, you will have a lot more scrap.

Permold Venting

In permanent molds for aluminum gravity, or in die-cast molds, the displacement of the air in the cavity represents a real problem because the mold is solid metal (usually cast iron) and has "0" permeability.

Permeability is defined as the ability to pass a gas or a liquid through a material. Even with slush molds for lead items or bullet molds for muzzle loading runs, the cast must be vented somehow.

The usual system is to place plug vents at the points where you feel the air will be trapped and put up back pressure or escape too slowly, preventing that section of the mold from filling. This vent is made by drilling a hole through from the cavity to the outside and filling, or *plugging*, the hole with a square rod. The hole is drilled to take a round rod very tightly. The rod is then filed on all four sides with a flat. This squared-up rod is then driven into place and dressed off to fit the internal contour of the cavity where it is installed. See Fig. 7-10. This method gives you one or more places between the plug and the hole in the mold for the passage of air.

Some operators will make a permold, pour a sample, and from the sample decide where, what size, and how many vents to install. In some cases, this procedure will simply move the defect to a new spot, and you will spend some time chasing it around. I have seen permolds riddled with vents only to find you really needed to have only a few vents and to pour the metal a little hotter, run the mold a little hotter, or both.

Parting line vents are common with gravity-poured or low-pressure permolds, such as automobile piston molds, toy soldiers,

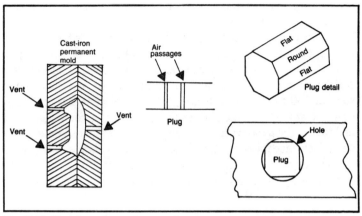

Fig. 7-10. How to make a plug vent in a permanent-mold cavity.

muzzle loading shot or automobile wheel weights. In this case, the mold has a series of grooves from the cavity to the outside of one or both mold halves. This process leaves many tiny passages for the air in the mold to escape. See Fig. 7-11.

As with plug vents, the smallness of the air passages, the sur-

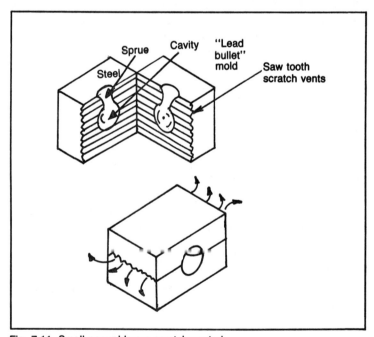

Fig. 7-11. Small permolds are scratch vented.

face tension of the metal, and the chilling effect of the mold will keep the metal from entering or running out of the vents.

Green Sand Scratch Vents

Some molders will scratch vents from near the cavity to the outer sand edge of the mold with the nose of their finishing trowel or a vent wire. This is a good practice for two reasons. When molding with loose patterns, you swab around the pattern prior to drawing it with your bulb sponge and so add a lot of moisture to sand all around the pattern. Where the body might have 6 percent or less moisture content, this area of swabbing is 40 percent or more. When the metal coming in the mold hits the parting line, it will blow and fuse with the steam generation because of this extra-wet sand area. Now with suitable scratch vents between the cope and drag joint, this steam will take the path of least resistance away from the molten metal and out. Without this path and where the molder was overzealous with the swab, it will back up into the casting, resulting in what is known as a *swabbing blow*, or *swabbing porosity*. See Fig. 7-12.

The other reason it is good practice to scratch vent, is that it adds to the overall venting. Remember that when you heat air, it expands, building up pressure; and with water you generate steam pressure. If you mold with high moisture and low permeability and ram it hard enough then pour it full of hot metal, you can actually have a bomb on your hands and wind up covered with hot metal and hot sand, to say the least.

Hot Shortness

We have talked about the permeability, mold hardness, moisture, venting, sand fineness, etc. Another problem with aluminum is *hot shortness*, sometimes simply referred to as hot short, which is a very low strength at elevated temperature.

At the temperature just below the solidification point of some aluminum alloys, the metal is extremely weak. The aluminum-copper alloys are much more hot short than most. Aluminum-silicon alloys are much less hot short than most, especially if the copper is kept below 5 percent of the alloy.

If a metal is hot short and is restricted excessively in its movement in the mold cavity as it shrinks from the solidification point to room temperature, when it passes through the temperature where it is at its weakest (hot short) point, something has to give.

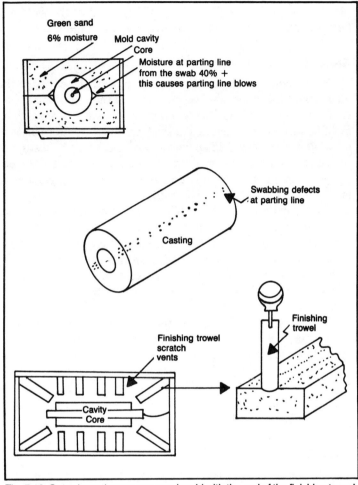

Fig. 7-12. Scratch venting a green sand mold with the end of the finishing trowel.

If the mold or a core will not give, the casting will actually tear and break. Hard ramming, bad casting design, and a molding sand that is too strong in hot strength is usually the cause of cracking, hot tearing, or other hot short defects. A core with too high of a hot strength is strong in compression strength at too high of a temperature. In other words, if you have a core that fails to break down and start collapsing before the casting around it reaches its hot short temperature, the casting will rupture.

You must have free casting movement before and through its hot-short temperature range. The problem is accelerated with

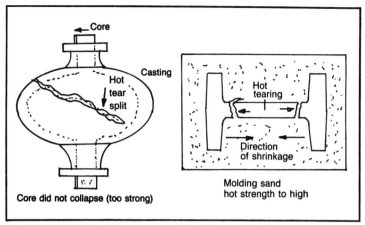

Fig. 7-13. Hot tearing in a green sand mold caused by the core.

aluminum because of its light weight and low pouring temperature. If a core is made with excessive binder, and insufficient heat is generated, or imparted to that core, to break down the binder soon enough, the resistance of the core to the contracting metal will cause a hot tear. The same goes for the molding sand. See Fig. 7-13.

Since aluminum is hot short, let's look carefully at the causes of hot tearing problems.

■ Design. There is a lack of fillets, or the fillets are too small. See Fig. 7-14.

■ An abrupt section change causes a wide variation in cooling rate. See Fig. 7-15.

■ If the sand has a low collapsibility because of excessive strength (green or dry) or has excessive carbonaceous material in the sand (graphite, seacoal, carbon), or if the clay in the sand bakes up hard at fairly low temperatures, you will have excessive hot strength. You don't want a mold that, when heated by the incoming metal, bakes itself into an ungiving brick. Sometimes with a natural sand, you will have elements in the sand that will vitrify the mold into a hard mass.

I have seen a reference stating that an aluminum sand containing farinaceous materials will result in hot tearing. Simply put, it refers to materials containing a lot of starch or having a mealy or powdery texture, such as dust, sand, shingle, sawdust, grit, meal, or bran flour. If your sand has too high of a hot strength which results in a low collapsibility, regardless of the reason, you are in trouble.

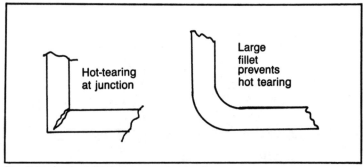

Fig. 7-14. Lack of filleting causes hot tearing.

■ If you ram the mold too hard, you can get into hot tearing.

■ If you pour too cold, not enough heat is produced in the mold to destroy the hot strength it has. If you have a core which is almost totally surrounded by the casting, and the casting is quite thin, it chills fast and does not produce enough heat nor for a long enough period to break down the core binders and allow the core to collapse. See Fig. 7-16.

Figure 7-16A shows a cutaway view of a thin-walled hollow ball casting with hot tearing. In this case, the core is almost surrounded by metal. When the casting started to shrink in all directions toward the core, the core prevented it from doing so, causing the casting to actually tear itself apart. In Fig. 7-16B, the same casting is shown without hot tearing defects. In Fig. 7-16A the core mix was suitable for heavy brass or light cast iron, but was much

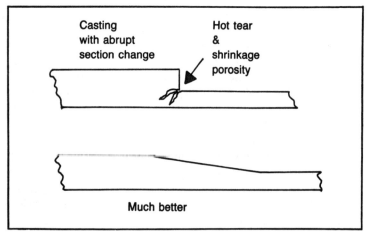

Fig. 7-15. Bad design causes hot tearing and/or shrinkage porosity.

134

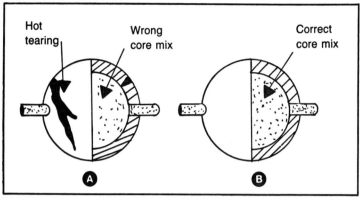

Fig. 7-16. Improper core mix causes hot tearing.

too high in hot strength. The core in B had the right mix where the hot strength was just high enough to let the casting solidify; then the core started coming unglued and collapsed.

You might have a core that does not cause a hot tear or any defect whatsoever but has just enough hot strength that it breaks down only far enough from its surface that the remaining portion of the core is next to impossible to remove through the space left by the core prints. This can be a real problem in a complicated interior configuration, such as a water-cooled engine head or a manifold casting. In the case of our ball, if you have a large section of uncollapsed core in the ball, you are going to have to break it up through the prints. See Fig. 7-17.

This problem also occurs with cast-iron motor blocks, heads, and steam radiators. In this type of work, you must actually be able to pour the heat-destroyed core out, as you could if the cavities were simply filled with dry, unbonded silica sand.

The whole problem is one of time and heat. The core must hold

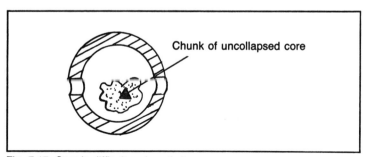

Fig. 7-17. Core is difficult and costly to remove.

together until the casting is set up enough to retain its intended shape. Once this is accomplished the heat from the casting must be sufficient to destroy the binder which holds the individual grains of sand together, letting the core actually fall apart. If the core should break down too soon, while the metal is still liquid, or too late, you have a big mess.

With cast iron, if you have a good casting, but it is full of lumps of core which you cannot get out, you can heat the casting up in an oven at a high enough temperature and hold it there long enough to break down the core binder in the offending pieces of lumps of core. With aluminum you could melt or warp the casting trying this procedure.

Hot tearing is a major problem with aluminum castings, and most information about casting aluminum simply skips over the subject of hot tearing with a simple definition of what the defect is called and what it looks like. As I stated, the design of the casting has a lot to do with how collapsible the core or molding sand must be. With the ball casting in Fig. 7-16, we must have maximum collapsibility of the internal core because the casting is shrinking toward the core but away from the mold in all directions; so the mold proper, even if it were on the high side of hot strength, should present little, if any, problem (Fig. 7-18).

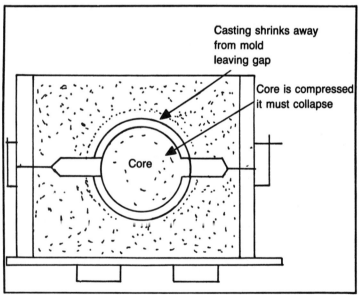

Fig. 7-18. Casting shrinks toward core and away from mold.

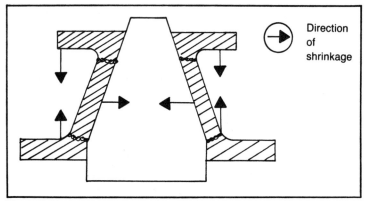

Fig. 7-19. Hard core causes no problem because of design, but high hot-strength molding sand causes hot tearing.

Let's look at a casting where the excessive hot strength of the core would be a much minor problem than the hot strength of the molding sand. Assume that you have sufficient permeability, and the mold is not too wet or rammed too hard, but the sand has an excessive hot strength. In the casting shown in Fig. 7-19, you can get into trouble with hot tears between the flanges in green sand. Because the core is heavily tapered, the casting will move up the core, thus producing a release.

Another method of preventing hot tears, particularly with large castings, is to hollow the core out so that it is only a shell and not a solid barrier to the shrinking metal. Even in some cases where the hot strength is excessive, with this method the core will collapse inward. See Fig. 7-20.

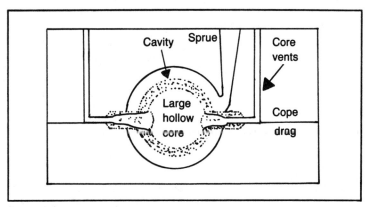

Fig. 7-20. Large cores should be hollow to assist in collapsibility, removal, etc.

Another advantage with hollow cores is that the gas generated by the core has an easy path of escape into the core's hollow interior and through the vents. You also use less core material, and thin cores bake quicker, costing you less in material, fuel, and time. Table 7-1 shows a few suitable core mixes for aluminum.

There are a maze of different core binders: furan no bake, carbon dioxide gaseous mixes of core sand and silicate of soda, ce-

Table 7-1. Aluminum Core Mixes.

Use	Ingredients
Heavy Castings:	Sharp silica sand 30 parts - New natural bonded molding sand 10 parts - Wheat flour 2 parts - Temper with molasses water (1 part molasses 10 parts water).
Medium Weight Castings:	Sharp sand 10 parts - New Molding sand 5 parts - Wheat flour 1 part. Temper with molasses water.
Long Skinny Cores:	Sharp sand 8 qts. - Wheat flour 1 qt. - Core oil 1/8 pint. (Core oil can be LinOil or a double boiled linseed oil).
For a Quick collapse core:	Sharp sand 45 parts - Molding sand 45 parts - Powdered resin (pine rosin) - Wheat flour 1 part
Small Cores:	Sharp sand 25 qts. - Molding sand 15 qts. - Linseed oil 1 qt.

A general purpose mix for large or small castings where you wish a smooth surface, you can control the dry strength and control the collapsibility via the amount of linseed oil. Note: The mix given below shows the linseed oil at from .2 qt to .5 qt per 100 lbs. of core sand.

General Purpose Mix:	100 lbs. of sharp sand - .8 lbs. of cereal flour (corn flour) - .2 to .5 qts. of linseed oil (your control) - 2 qts. of water - .2 qt. of kerosene. A little kerosene in any core mix using a core oil or linseed oil is beneficial and helps to keep the core from sticking in the core box. It also helps distribute the core oil evenly through the mix.

Cores requiring a high green strength with a medium permeability: 100 lbs. of sharp sand - .9 lb. dextrine base dry binder - .7 qt. linseed oil - 3.5 qts. water.

Blow Mix:	100 lbs. sharp silica - 1 lb. corn flour - .4 qt. linseed oil - 1.5 qts. water - .2 qt. kerosene.

ment sand cores, etc. Some of these, especially carbon dioxide and furan cores, require special additives to get them to collapse at the low temperature of aluminum casting, presenting a problem you can do without. There is nothing wrong with a core binder, such as a vegetable drying oil, natural and synthetic resins, cereals, proteins, linseed oil, or combinations of these materials.

The big advantage of the small or backyard caster is he can buy some linseed oil and kerosene from the paint supply company, some flour from the baker, and some sand from the building supply company or the beach.

Deformed Alloys

What about the alloys that do not tear? If you have excessive hot strength in your molding sand or cores, or the design is conducive to restricted movement problems, you simply have a new problem. It will stretch and deform instead of tearing. See Fig. 7-21.

Some people have a problem with proper classification of a defect. You must not confuse a shrink crack (shrinkage porosity) with a hot tear defect. A *hot tear* is a strain fracture that happens during the solidification and shrinking of the casting where the movement of the casting is restricted. A *shrinkage crack* is due to lack of feed metal, risers, etc., where a liquid section is cut off from the necessary liquid feed reservoir and acts as a feeder for a thinner section. There is a lack of proper progressive solidification from the thin sections to the gates and feed risers. See Fig. 7-22.

As I stated, poor design is a big factor as far as scrap is concerned. It must be given close attention. For a few examples see Fig. 7-23.

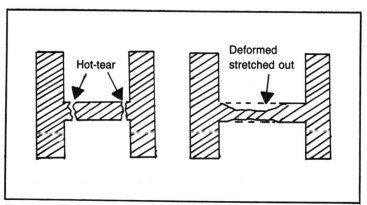

Fig. 7-21. Some alloys will be subject to deforming and/or hot tearing.

MOLDING SANDS FOR ALUMINUM

Let's look at a few suitable molding sands that should do a good job. For years Sam Pitre Jr. and I cast both aluminum and brass in natural-bonded river sand from the banks along the Mississippi River and the Red River near Alexandria, Louisiana. On heavy work, we simply used 100-mesh washed and dried silica sand, bonded with 4 percent Southern Bentonite.

For very fine detail on light aluminum, you can use *Windsor Locks*, a natural bonded sand that is very fine and flourlike. It has an average grain fineness of 270, a permeability about 10, and a green strength about 7. Albany natural-bonded sands can be purchased in a wide classification for aluminum—Albany #00 for very fine small work, #0 for medium work, and #1 for heavy work. There are also mixes you can make up yourself that will cover a large range of work.

A simple sand for light work is sharp sand, 99.5 percent by weight; wheat flour 0.5 percent by weight; and 5.5 percent water. This mix is rather weak but is great for small stuff. The green strength is about 5.0 PSI with a permeability of 18. I have successfully cast aluminum castings up to 40 pounds with this mix. For the base sand, I used washed and dried sharp silica 120 mesh.

Another mix that works fine with the same base sand is 74 percent sand by weight; 4.6 percent fire clay by weight; and 18.5 per-

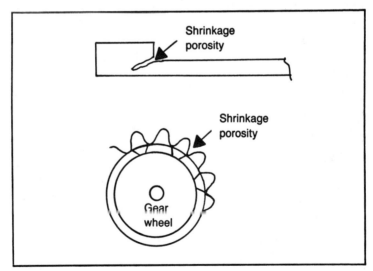

Fig. 7-22. Shrinkage porosity, often confused with hot tearing, is a common problem with gear wheels at the tooth junction.

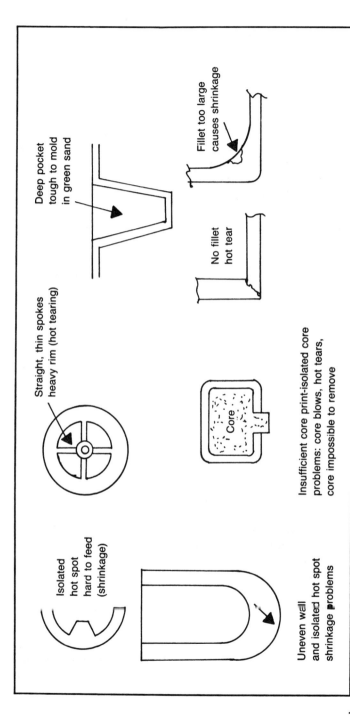

Deep pocket tough to mold in green sand

Fillet too large causes shrinkage

No fillet hot tear

Straight, thin spokes heavy rim (hot tearing)

Core

Insufficient core print-isolated core problems: core blows, hot tears, core impossible to remove

Isolated hot spot hard to feed (shrinkage)

Uneven wall and isolated hot spot shrinkage problems

Fig. 7-23. Poor design is responsible for much scrap.

141

cent silica flour by weight. Temper 5.5 to 6 percent moisture. The green compression will run from 8 to 10 PSI, and the perm 20 to 30. This mix is great for aluminum from 1 ounce to 20 pounds.

If you cannot locate a suitable natural-bonded molding sand, simply make your own. Write to the Cedar Heights Clay Co., for a sack of their yellow bonding clay (See Appendix C). Find some fine sharp sand, and you have both the sand and the binder. The company will also advise you about its various clays and their uses.

Petro Bond is an oil-bonded sand which is quite popular with small foundries for nonferrous castings. Some foundry supply houses will sell you a batch of Petro Bond sand all milled up and ready to go. Because the bond is an oil instead of water and clay, less gas is formed, and problems from blows are eliminated for the most part. Using oil in place of water allows you to use finer based sands with lower permeabilities and higher mold hardnesses for fine finishes. You can use a washed and dried, sharp silica sand from 120 to 180 fineness for casting aluminum.

The oil is the most important ingredient in making up a Petro Bond molding sand mix. Oils containing inhibitors or detergents, such as special industrial oils and automobile oils, cannot be used because the additives interfere with the Petro Bond reaction. You need the old-time, conventionally refined oil, that is, just oil, nothing else.

This type of oil is available from dealers all over the country, as well as most foundry supply companies. The catalyst used is called P-1 and is produced by the Baroid Division of NL industries. This company will also supply the oil and instructions.

The P-1 catalyst seems to be basically methanol (methyl alcohol or, wood alcohol). The Petro Bond, according to Baroid Co., is a formulated material that acts as a sand bonding agent in the presence of oil and the P-1 catalyst.

A typical batch of Petro Bond sand for aluminum is 100 pounds washed and dried silica sand, 120 to 180 fineness; 5 1/2 pounds Petro Bond binder; 2 pounds Petro Bond oil, approx. 2 pints; and 1 ounce P-1 catalyst. Mull the sand and the Petro Bond for one minute; then add the oil and mull for 10 minutes. Next add the P-1 and mull for 3 to 5 minutes.

One small aluminum foundry I know told me that they have worked up a good oil-bonded sand consisting of 100 pounds sharp sand; 5 pounds iron oxide; 2 pounds metro 20 oil from Mobil Oil Co.; and 1 ounce methanol. I haven't tried this formula, but I have tried the conventional Petro-Bonded sand for aluminum at mold hardnesses of 80 or more with great results. You must have a muller to keep it in shape. You can mix it in a small cement mixer. Remove the blades, weld up the holes, and throw the sand in with a couple of ignots to do the mixing. It works well as a simple muller for Petro Bond, natural-bonded sands, core sand mixes, etc. I use a small ¼ horsepower cement mixer.

With brass, I found the Petro-Bond molds smoked to high heaven when poured, and for quite a while had a very pungent, irritating fume. With aluminum this problem was minor because of the low pouring temperature; so I could put up with it.

The advantage I found was, if you are only producing castings now and again, the Petro Bond sand is always ready. It does not sit around and dry out. You must have a muller of some sort, however, to keep it in shape, but you don't need to mull it after each use. You can reuse it for quite a few castings by simply recutting it with a shovel or running it through a ¼ riddle between castings. When it gets too weak to work, throw it into the mixer and add some oil, Petro Bond, and catalyst and rebond it.

The typical properties of the Petro Bond sand are: green strength, 12 PSI; permeability, 15; and flowability, 87. The collapsibility is great for aluminum; there are little problems with hot tearing. I am not endorsing this product, but it might be just what you need.

There is not really a problem with natural bonding sand drying out between uses. Once you have your sand tempered to the degree you desire, keep it covered with a sheet of plastic between uses. This way it will not lose its moisture but simply set there and percolate.

After you have poured your molds, shake out the castings. Wet the shake-out sand with a sprinkling can and riddle it, throw the plastic over your heap, and hold down the edges of the plastic with ingots or whatever. You will find that the hot sand from casting will steam under the plastic, keeping it in great shape. If you do this, you will find that you can come back a month later, uncover your sand, and start molding. There will be no back-breaking cutting and riddling, as you try to retemper your heap. You will also find that after only one night under the plastic, the temper water in your sand is distributed evenly throughout the heat.

CORE PRACTICE

You will find that the mixes called out in the section on hot shortness will give you a good starting point for making cores. As

143

with any practice, it is impossible to call out a mix for everything you might wish to design. You must have a base to work from, then vary your mix to suit the job. One very common problem you can run into is having too many different mixes. I have worked in foundries that have a different mix for almost every job they run, when in fact they could have reduced the total down to two basic mixes, one for light work and one for heavy work, or three at the most.

Green Sand Cores

Another route which is often overlooked, or completely ignored, is the use of green sand cores. (I do not mean the green sand core left by the pattern.) See Fig. 7-24. These cores are made separately in a core box just as you would make them with a dry sand core mix, but using green molding sand in place of a core mix. Let's take a simple example. We are casting some simple, small, flanged bushings from a split pattern that requires a core through the bore.

Figure 7-25 shows a simple split pattern and a full core box for the bore. Your first thought would be to make up the needed cores in a dry sand mix and bake the cores in the core oven, or perhaps make the cores in one of the available no-bake mixes, such as furan. You can, however, simply ram up the core with green molding sand, the same sand with which you are molding. Let's take it step-by-step.

Temper enough green sand to do the job a little damper than you would for molding, then shake it through a #16 riddle. Dust

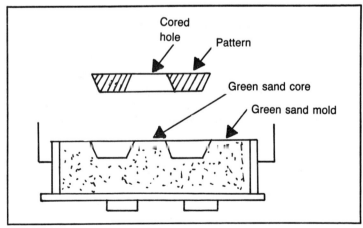

Fig. 7-24. Green sand core left by pattern.

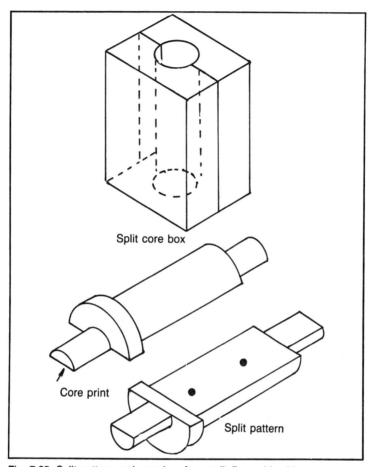

Split core box

Core print

Split pattern

Fig. 7-25. Split pattern and core box for small, flanged bushing.

the core box with a little walnut-shell dry parting and clamp it with a C clamp. Now ram up the core in the same manner you would with a dry sand core mix—using a dowel and adding the sand in small increments and hot ramming too hard between additions; otherwise you will get a natural parting. See Fig. 7-26.

The core is vented with a vent wire. Then it is removed from the box by placing the box on a core plate and rapping it lightly. Remove one side of the box and slide the core with the remaining half box to the desired location on the plate. Repeat this until the desired number of cores are on the plate. See Fig. 7-27.

The green sand cores are now baked at 350 to 400 degrees Fahrenheit until they are bone dry. Remove them from the oven

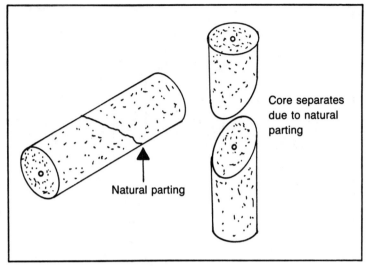

Fig. 7-26. A green sand core improperly rammed results in a natural parting.

on the core plate. Now here's the trick. As soon as the cores are removed from the oven, while they are quite hot, you spray them all over with a mixture of molasses and water—1 part blackstrap molasses and 9 to 10 parts water. Use a fine spray. The heat from the cores will bake the molasses/water coating to a hard, dry skin on the cores. Let the cores cool to room temperature, and you will be surprised as to how tough they are and easy to handle. The skin-dried surface prevents the core from washing during pouring and prevents erosion or damage when handling them to set them in the prints. See Fig. 7-28.

Because this kind of core has only baked clay (the molding sand binder) to furnish the bond and a minute amount of sugar from the molasses on the skin, and you have removed all the free moisture by baking, these cores will cause no problem with wet blows. You can, however, have hot tearing if the hot dry strength is excessive, and the core does not collapse soon enough or readily. If this is the case, you can add a bit of sea coal to your green sand and/or use less temper water.

In a great many cases, you can use unbaked green sand cores. Jewelers who sand-cast rings and mountings go this way. The mold is made, and the core is rammed up, using a tube for a core box. The inner diameter of the tube is the same dimension as the outer diameter of the ring pattern print. The tube is longer than the desired core. It is rammed up fairly tightly, and the core is remov-

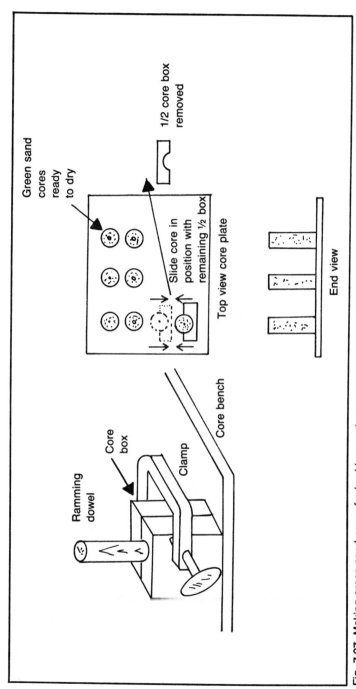

Fig. 7-27. Making green sand cores for bushing casting.

147

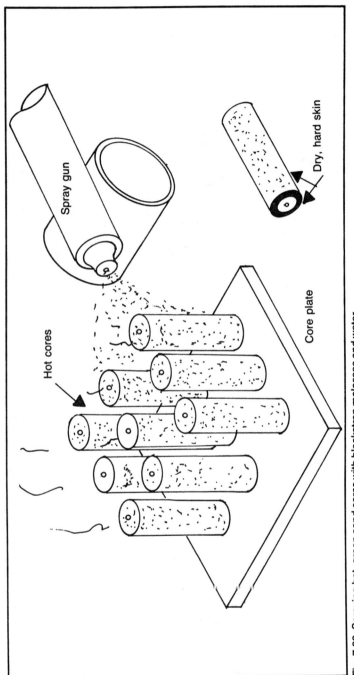

Fig. 7-28. Spraying hot, green sand cores with blackstrap molasses and water.

Spray gun

Dry, hard skin

Hot cores

Core plate

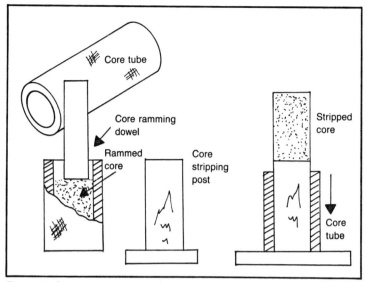

Fig. 7-29. Green sand core produced in a tube-core box.

ed by a stripper dowel which has the same outer diameter as the pattern print.

The tube is pressed down on the stripper dowel, leaving the core setting on top of this dowel. Now, by carefully tipping the core over with the first finger, it can be picked up between the thumb and first finger on the ends and then set into the mold. See Fig. 7-29.

Of course, you can also oven-dry and spray these tube-made cores if you like. There are all sorts of things you can do with green sand dried and sprayed cores. In some cases, the cores can be quite complicated. With a job you run every now and again (a repeat job) you can often well afford to build special core arbors of lifting plates,

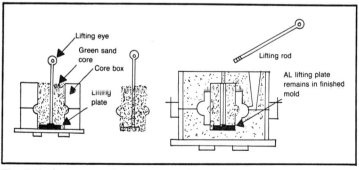

Fig. 7-30. A green sand core supported by a lifting plate.

149

etc., to facilitate handling, setting, and drying. An example is shown in Fig. 7-30.

A cast-aluminum lifting plate is made with a threaded lifting boss in its center and a corresponding lifting eye threaded to match the lifting plate thread. In practice, the core box is clamped, and the lifting plate with lifting eye screwed in place is placed in the box. The core is rammed and the box removed. The core is not handled by the eye, dried, and sprayed. It is set in place in the mold using the eye to lower it in place. The eye is unscrewed and drawn from the core, leaving a core vent. The cope is set, and the mold poured. The lifting plate remains in the mold during pouring.

There are all sorts or arbors, crabs, lifting plates, etc., that you can make to facilitate the use of green sand cores or dry green sand cores. Extremely small, round cores can be made with tinned steel tubes available from any foundry supply company or chaplet supplier. In this case, you simply fill the tube with lightly rammed green sand. The tube remains in the casting. See Fig. 7-31.

Smith & Richardson Mfg. Co. can supply you with all sorts of hinge tubes and related items that will save you time and money. Ask for Catalog 175.

The advantages to using green sand cores are basically their low cost, the fact that they will not contaminate your heap sand, and that there are less problems with blows, scabs, etc. With green or oil dry sand cores, flanged (perforated) tubes can be used to both reinforce and vent a core. See Fig. 7-32.

Characteristics of the Core

There are really no fixed rules to follow with cores because

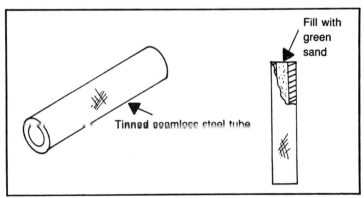

Fig. 7-31. Core tubes for coring small-diameter holes.

150

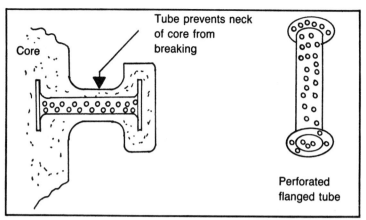

Fig. 7-32. Perforated flanged tubes to support the core.

of the unlimited design of aluminum castings. The characteristics of the core are important.

■ The green core must be able to resist breakage and deformation during handling from the core bench to the oven.

■ The baked core must also be able to resist breakage or abrasion from the oven to placement in the mold.

■ During pouring, the core must soften, or collapse, soon enough, but not too soon or too late, to avoid hot tears. It should also collapse sufficiently by the time the casting reaches room temperature so that it can be easily removed.

You must control the green strength, dry strength, tensile strength, surface hardness, hot strength, and retained strength to accomplish these characteristics in a core. The core must also have sufficient permeability so that it can vent off the gas produced by the core binders as they are heated during pouring.

The permeability is controlled by the fineness of the core sand, as is the surface smoothness. You should, therefore, use as coarse a sand as is consistant with the desired surface smoothness; it should not be so fine that it causes blows or gas porosity. Remember what I said about a gas: whether it is steam, core gas, or whatever, it will take the shortest path of least resistance. See Fig. 7-33.

You must also remember that, if you use excessive binders, the core will produce so much gas so quickly at a high pressure that regardless of the size of the sand grain you will have core blows and a porous casting, as well as an excessively high hot strength,

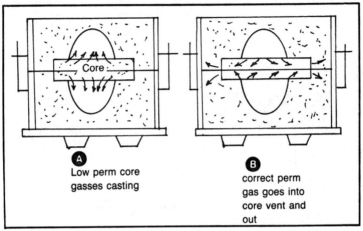

Fig. 7-33. Core permeability is too low (A); correct permeability (B).

resulting in hot tears. Looking at the other side of the coin, if the core is underbonded, with too low of a hot strength, it will collapse too soon, before the casting has solidified sufficiently, resulting in a real mess. In some cases, the cored section will consist of a mixture of sand and aluminum in place of a cavity.

If the core is too weak, the surface will also wash away during pouring, distributing sand throughout the casting, as well as causing metal penetration. The problem of metal actually penetrating the surface of the core is also caused by a core that was rammed too soft when it was made, resulting in a loose, porous, disjointed structure when baked. See Fig. 7-34. This defect is often mistaken as a scab defect.

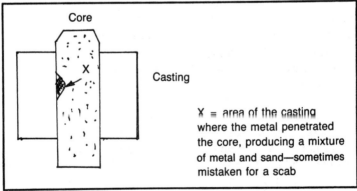

Fig. 7-34. Soft spot in core is penetrated by molten metal.

You have many factors to consider: the amount of surface area of the core in contact with the molten metal, how long it is in contact, the amount of gas produced by the core, and at what pressure.

Let's talk about this problem a bit. Let's say you are using a binder such as pitch or a resin. With this type of binder, when the core is baked, the binder melts; and when the core cools to room temperature, the binder hardens, cementing the sand grains together.

Now, when the mold is poured with a pitch or resin type of binder core, you will note that at first there seems to be little or no gas coming from the core vents; then there are huge volumes of stinky core gas evident, especially with a pitch binder such as Gilsonite. The resulting casting is, however, free from core blows and gas porosity. The reason is that a resin- or pitch-bonded core, although producing great volumes of gas due to its latent gas content, usually only produces the gas after the casting has set up, or at least has a solidified skin through which the gas cannot penetrate. This delayed action of considerable gas generation is of a relatively low pressure.

You could have a binder which produces very little gas, but the generation of this gas is produced fast at high pressure early in the game; such a binder would be useless. It would be like pouring hot lead on a wet piece of steel, or sticking a wet skimmer into a pot of molten metal; it's more of an explosive deal. A pitch-bonded core will gas and smoke for hours after the casting is rock hard.

Binders for baked cores are produced chiefly from vegetable drying oils, petroleum derivatives, natural and synthetic resins, cereals, proteins, pitch, or various mixtures and combinations of these materials. You should keep the binders at a minimum, using no more than is necessary to give you a core that will bake throughout and collapse soon enough.

The surface smoothness of cores is determined primarily by the fineness or coarseness of the core sand used. It is a give-and-take proposition between permeability and smoothness.

One thing that always amazed me was to the see the cored interior of, say a gear box casting, which had a surface as smooth as glass, although this area of the casting was completely out of sight, on the finished product. Smoothness is usually for cosmetic appearance. Also you will find castings such as bushing stock, which is to be machined both inside and out, glass smooth.

If you require an extremely smooth surface on a cored surface, you are more often than not better off to use an open, coarse-grained

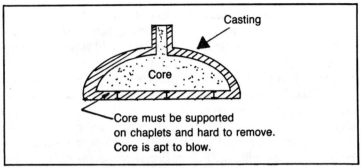

Fig. 7-35. Core removal is a tough, costly proposition.

core sand in order to get excellent permeability, venting, and collapsibility; and then simply use a good, smooth core wash to give the core the desired surface finish. When you have a design where the core is almost completely surrounded by metal with small prints, you are faced with two problems: getting the core gas vented out, and removing the core from the casting. Make no mistake about it: dry sand core removal can be a considerable portion of your cost, in time and labor to produce the casting. Let's look at an example.

In Fig. 7-35, I left only a small opening at the top through which to bring a core print and vent off the core gas, and there is no way to support this core other than with chaplets. There is a problem in how to break this core up and shake it all out of the top opening. This method could result in blows and hot tearing when we pour it. If the chaplets don't fuse, we have another problem. The solution is to make this casting two castings, eliminate the core all together, and bolt it together. You can bet it will cost a lot less to go this way. See Fig. 7-36.

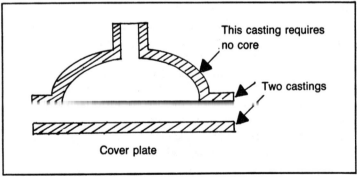

Fig. 7-36. The solution to poor design is shown in Fig. 7-35.

154

Furan Cores

Furan no-bake cores are sometimes a great time saver, and they can be made up in the core box for a complicated core which would otherwise require dryers or bedding to transfer and support it during baking. You simply let them set up in the core box then remove them. You also do not have the expense of baking nor the time to bake and cool.

There are also disadvantages. Once you have added the binder to the sand containing the catalyst, you have to work quickly. Things start to set up, and it has a limited bench life once it is mixed. The binder and the catalyst are expensive. It is corrosive to your skin because the catalyst is phosphoric acid. If you do not use gloves to make the cores, you soon wind up with very brown, discolored hands. The discoloration will not wash off but must wear off. The fumes irritate both the lungs and the eyes.

Phosphoric acid 75 percent (liquid) is toxic by ingestion and inhalation. It irritates the eyes and the skin. The toxic maximum tolerance is 1 milligram per cubic meter of air.

The binder is furfural alcohol, ureas, and a formaldehyde. This is the prime material used in the formulation of furan resins. Basically what you have is a liquid synthetic resin that, when catalyzed with acidic materials, forms a tough, resinous film that glues the sand grains together. The reaction simply is:

liquid resin (furfural alcohol) + catalyst (phosphoric acid)
= solid resin + H_2O (water) + heat.

The speed of the reaction depends upon several factors, such as the type of sand and its temperature, speed and type of mixing equipment, type of binder formulation, and type and amount of catalyst used. The binder formulation varies with the manufacturer, but it basically consists of furfural alcohol, ureas, and formaldehyde. The difference is in the combinations of these ingredients.

Furfural is prepared from a large family of cellulous products, such as corn cobs and oat hulls. It is a product derived by the distillation of the cellulous product with diluted sulphuric acid. You wind up with an oily liquid with an aromatic odor. The next step is the catalytic hydrogenation of the furfural to give you furfural alcohol, an amber-colored liquid. Now add ureas, and you have the no-bake binder. Furfural is often called an oil, brand oil, or furyl carbinol.

The furfural alcohol itself automatically polymerizes with an acid catalyst, often with explosive violence. What you purchase for your foundry is this alcohol which has been modified with ureas and formaldehyde.

The core mix is quite simple: washed and dried core sand (sharp silica); 2 percent furan resin (binder); and 40 percent phosphoric acid 75 percent (catalyst). This 40 percent is based on the weight of the binder used. If you have 100 pounds of sand, you need 2 pounds of binder and 40 percent of 2 pounds, or .8 pounds of phosphoric acid.

This is simply a basic mix which you can vary to suit yourself. I find that 2 percent binder against 25 percent acid gives you more time to work. Five gallons of furan no-bake binder and a gallon of 75 percent phosphoric acid are handy to have for that special core or mold for the small foundry.

You must add the acid to the sand first and mix well, then add the binder and mix well. If you add the binder before the acid, you will get uneven, spotty curings and segregation. Some sand will not be bonded at all, and spots or sections will be overbonded.

The mix is rammed into the core box and stripped as soon as it has developed enough strength to hold together. The core goes from an amber color to a green color to a green so dark it appears black.

You cannot use core boxes that have been shellacked or painted because the reaction of the binder and acid in setting up produces heat, which will melt the pattern or coating. The result is a real mess and a rough surface on the core or pattern, and in some cases it is impossible to remove the core from the box or the pattern from a no-bake mold. With a pair of rubber gloves, you can easily mix small batches in a plastic bucket by hand as needed. Do it outside or in a well-ventilated area, however.

Collapsibility can be a problem with no-bake molds because aluminum is poured at a relatively low temperature, not generating enough heat to destroy the resin fast enough or completely enough, producing hot tearing and tough core removal. Therefore you should bond as lightly as possible, using low hot-strength cores.

BREAKDOWN AOOCLCnATOnO

Breakdown accelerators are available to improve the collapsibility of both oil sand cores and no-bake, resin-bonded cores. These products are mostly powdered alkali metal compounds which promote thermal decomposition of the resins at temperatures above 752 degrees Fahrenheit. Below this temperature, the accelerator does not affect the binder or the catalyst. To remove the core completely (reduce it to powder), the castings must be heated above 932 degrees Centigrade in an oven for several hours in order for the accelerator to break down the binder. Below this temperature, nothing happens.

GATES AND RISERS

Metal casting practice is not only simple, but is a very basic principle. It is called progressive directional solidification by controlling the temperature gradients. If the casting design is such that it will not do its thing by progressive directional solidification, you must make it do so with risers, chills, gates, pressure, centrifugal force, etc. If you understand the principles, a good blueprint of the casting will provide you with all the information you need to design your gating and risering system. (Regardless of how you gate the casting, you must prevent the inclusion of aluminum oxides and nonmetallic ingredients) from the casting. I have already discussed in some detail how easily aluminum metal is reverted back to aluminum oxide because of its very high affinity with oxygen. Aluminum has a specific gravity of 2.7, and aluminum oxide has a specific gravity of 3.4 to 4. Because these two gravities are so close together, a sink or float separation becomes difficult at best. If, therefore, you intend to eliminate aluminum oxide as far as possible from your castings, you should provide some effective way to filter the aluminum of these oxides and whatever nonmetallic ingredients you might have picked up on your way to the mold. In Chapter 2, I touched on this problem and the use of the steel wool as a filter, as well as ceramic filters. Oxide inclusions cannot really be beneficial in any way whatsoever; however, in most cases some oxide inclusions will be of little or no consequence.

If your melting practice is good, and you pour close to the sprue and keep the sprue choked throughout the entire pour, you are usually home clean. Of course if your melting, handling, and gating practices are sloppy, a filter will not offset them. I have found that the regular dry sand and ceramic strainer cores, which are commonly used with red brass, when used with aluminum simply assure you of oxide inclusions in the casting. See Fig. 7-37.

If you pour the aluminum through a strainer core, you simply divide the stream up by the number of holes in the strainer core, increasing the exposed surface area of the incoming aluminum and setting yourself up for some real nice oxide formation.

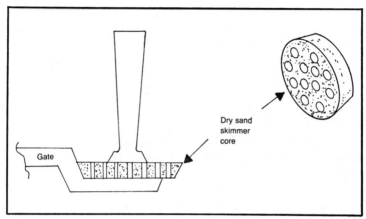

Fig. 7-37. Strainer cores are not recommended for aluminum.

It is a fact that, as the aluminum solidifies, it is necessary to provide liquid feed metal to feed the voids left by its reduction in volume during crystal formation in order to come up with a sound structure. The direction of the solidification is determined by temperature gradients; so in order to get directional solidification, you must control the temperature gradients. So, you want to be able to supply liquid feed metal to the casting as it solidifies and control the direction of this solidification so that the last things to solidify are the risers and feeders.

In other words, you must make sure that the solidification of the casting proceeds directionally to a pool of liquid metal from which it can feed to compensate for its loss in volume as it goes from a liquid to a solid. This volumetric shrinkage for aluminum varies with the alloy composition and the gas content, and it can be from as much as 9 percent in volume to as low as 2 to 3 percent.

Gradient is defined as the degree of inclination of a slope. So, what we have is a temperature slope. Figure 7-38 shows a correct progressive, directional solidification temperature gradient. Figure 7-39 shows a temperature gradient going the wrong way and resulting in a shrinkage defect because the large end of the casting is isolated from any reservoir of hot metal it can use to compensate for its volumetric shrinkage.

You will have a shrinkage defect regardless of how you gate a casting. All you have to do, then, is see to it that the defect is moved away from the casting and lands in a riser which you can remove and remelt. Suppose you needed a solid aluminum bushing stock 12 inches long and 3 inches in diameter, and you decided to

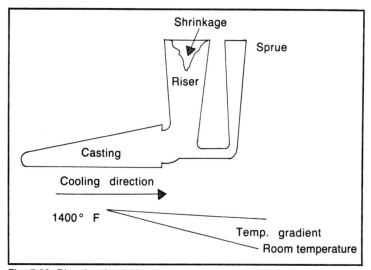

Fig. 7-38. Directional solidification temperature gradient.

simply turn a 3-inch diameter tapered pattern, and cast it open face with no gate or riser whatsoever. In Fig. 7-40 "A" is the open-faced mold. At "B" is shown the resulting casting from the 12-inch long

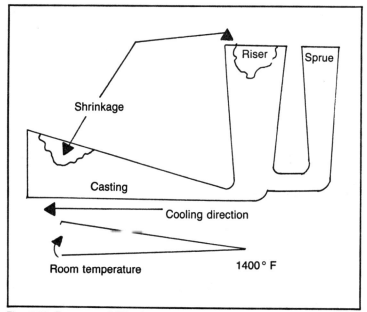

Fig. 7-39. Reverse solidification temperature gradient.

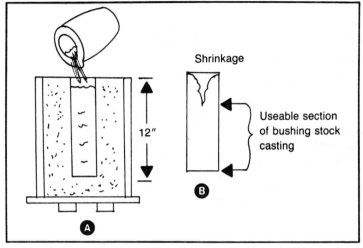

Fig. 7-40. You must provide a well of metal to feed the casting.

pattern. The resulting usable portion of the casting is far shorter than the desired 12 inches.

This is a classic example of progressive directional solidification as the casting is being poured. The first metal in the bottom starts to solidify, and its shrinkage is compensated by the hot liquid metal on top of it. As this portion solidifies, the hot metal above it provides liquid metal to feed until there is no longer any room to put feed metal, leaving the top portion of the bushing with no feed to replace the metal that the section below used to compensate for its volumetric shrinkage as it went from a liquid to a solid. See Fig. 7-41.

As I stated , you always have a volumetric shrinkage defect; so in order to get the desired shrink-free 12 inches desired, you must provide a reservoir of liquid feed metal for the casting. In its function of feeding the casting and not have a feed source of its own, the reservoir (riser) winds up with the shrinkage defect, and because you are not concerned with making solid defect-free gates and risers, you are home free.

The solution to the problem in Fig. 7-41 then, is quite simple. You supply the casting with feed metal to compensate for the shrinkage cavity. See Fig. 7-42.

Of course a casting should be designed with the actual casting process in mind, but this is always not done for various reasons. In some cases, the casting is designed by someone who doesn't know how a casting is produced, much less how the design affects

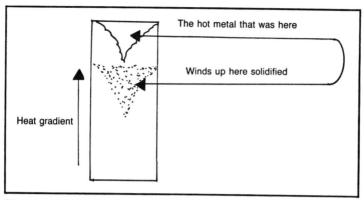

Fig. 7-41. Solidification voids are filled in by the hot liquid metal above these voids.

the outcome or the problems a design can present to the founder.
    Follow these rules:
    ■ Feed the heavy sections by placing risers there to provide a reservoir of hot liquid metal (Fig. 7-43).
    ■ Wherever possible, gate into the riser(s) so that it receives the hottest metal last. See Fig. 7-44.
    ■ Maintain direction solidification by maintaining a thermal gradient toward the risers. Use one or more chills to make sure that the solidification proceeds in the direction of the hot feed metal reservoir of the riser. See Fig. 7-45.

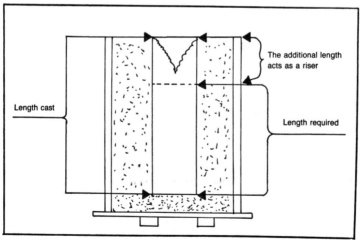

Fig. 7-42. By adding length to your bushing pattern, you move the shrinkage upward, giving you the desired length of solid material.

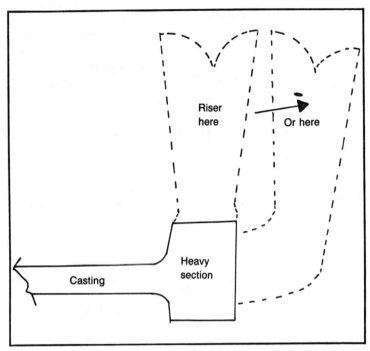

Fig. 7-43. Riser the heavy sections to feed them.

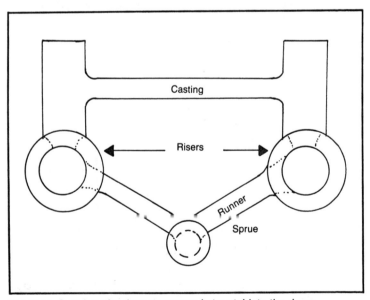

Fig. 7-44. Gate into the risers to ensure hot metal into the risers.

162

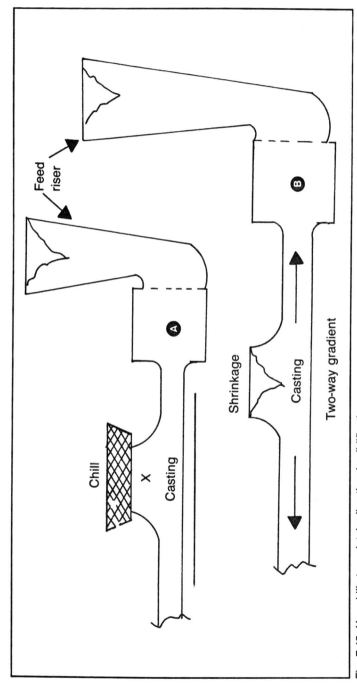

Fig. 7-45. Use chills to maintain directional solidification.

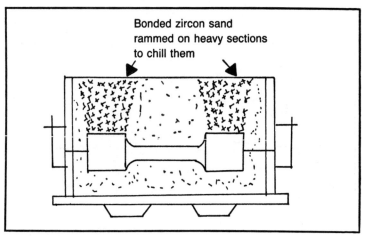

Fig. 7-46. Zircon sand used to chill a heavy section.

A chill at point x in Fig. 7-45A absorbs heat from the heavy section produced by the boss, making it solidify directionally along with the rest of the casting. Without the chill, the hot section at x will shrink as it attempts to feed the lighter sections around it, as shown in Fig. 7-45B.

Chills can be made of aluminum, cast iron, graphite, steel, brass, or bronze. In some cases, you can use a high heat-conducting material, such as silicon carbide or zircon sand, to make up the mold and provide the required chilling. See Fig. 7-46.

Zircon sand conducts the heat rapidly from its point of contact. It is widely used for this purpose, especially in sand-casting steel. A dry sand core made of zircon sand can be very beneficial in preventing shrinkage problems in areas such as a heavy hub on

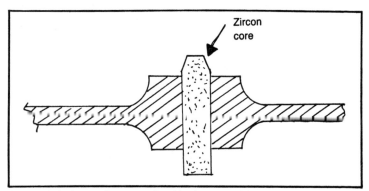

Fig. 7-47. A dry sand core made with zircon sand is used to chill the hub.

a gear blank or fly wheel, (Fig. 7-47). Chills can be extremely beneficial in reducing the size and number of risers required.

■ Be careful where you gate and riser; keep in mind that the gating system has to be removed.

■ Use multiple ingates on aluminum, especially on large-area, fairly thin work. Remember that the pouring temperature of aluminum is fairly low. If the metal has a long way to go to fill the mold and is cooling all the time, and you do not get the mold filled fast enough, you are going to wind up with a misrun. See Fig. 7-48.

■ If the casting is exceptionally large or long, you might have to pour several sprues at the same time from separate ladles in order to fill the mold fast enough to prevent a cold metal misrun. See Fig. 7-49.

■ Insulated risers help reduce the riser size you need by keeping the riser from chilling too fast, and thus keeping the metal liquid longer to provide feed metal. See Fig. 7-50.

■ Connect side risers as closely as possible to prevent the connecting link from freezing too soon and cutting off the liquid feed metal in the riser. See Fig. 7-51.

■ Remember the end point of solidification is at the riser or risers; they must solidify last to be effective.

POURING THE MOLD

Regardless of how well you have designed your gating and riser-

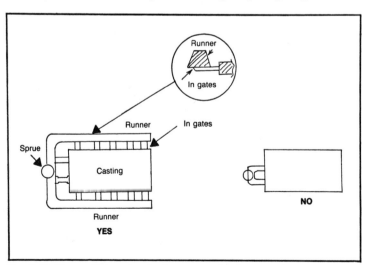

Fig. 7-48. Use multiple gates for large-area aluminum castings.

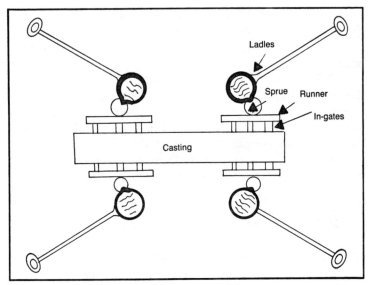

Fig. 7-49. Pouring a large casting with several ladles.

ing system and made your mold, if you do not pour the mold correctly, all is lost. As simple as pouring might appear, it is quite tricky. You must pour close to the sprue with one smooth movement, keeping the sprue full from start to finish without allowing

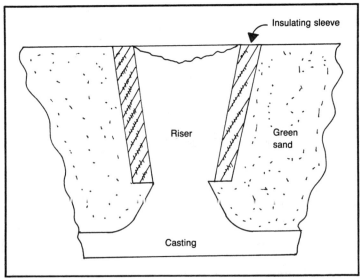

Fig. 7-50. An insulated riser stays hot and feeds longer.

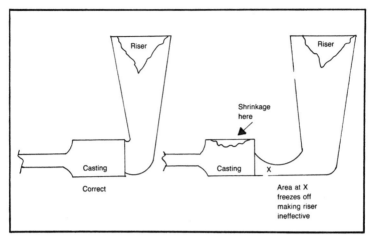

Fig. 7-51. Side risers must be connected close to the casting to be fully effective.

the stream velocity to be interrupted even for a moment. Now, I'm not talking about a discontinued or broken stream of metal during pouring, called *bobbling*; I'm talking about an uninterrupted stream of metal that changes its speed of entry into the gate system and the mold cavity.

Let's say the metal during the pouring of a mold is entering the cavity, etc., at 5 miles per hour at the start, and this velocity is slacked to 3.5 or 4.5 miles per hour, then increased to 5 miles per hour again. You come up with a misrun. Now, this might seem silly to you, but it's a fact. In many cases what happens is that the person who is pouring suddenly realizes that he is pouring faster than the sprue and system is able to take the metal; so he slacks off to prevent the metal from going all over the top of the mold and down his shoes.

Now, you must choke the sprue with the first splash of metal from the ladle, then pour as fast as the mold will take the metal without going over or under this velocity during the entire pouring. It takes a lot of experience to learn, and as I mentioned, it's not only tricky but deceiving. Years ago I ran a plumbing ware foundry and trained a good pour-off man. His scrap loss from pouring misruns was less then .05 percent, and when he was out the scrap jumped to 5 percent plus.

Often a foundry will run the same work day in and day out and then all at once the scrap starts to climb in leaps and bounds. They will often even change the gating on castings that they have cast by the hundreds, raise the pouring temperature, change the sand

167

etc., trying to find the problem, only to find it is the pour-off man. Of course, the gates, the molds, the pouring temperature, etc., must all be correct, but if you are getting good castings and start to lose them, especially to misruns without having changed anything, look at your pouring practice very closely.

You cannot judge the temperature of molten aluminum by eye. You must have a good pyrometer. The surface of molten aluminum remains unchanged between 1000 and 1300 degrees Fahrenheit. At 1000 degrees, aluminum can be fluid enough to pour a thick casting. You will lose a lot more castings pouring them too cold than too hot.

Other points to remember are:

■ You should not hold aluminum in the furnace for long periods of time; however, you can hold aluminum sometimes for 2 or more hours and still produce a good casting, if your pour the mold correctly and at the correct temperature. Don't disturb the dross on the crucible until you are ready to pour.

■ You will find various fluxes for sale, but the one that has stood the test of time is zinc chloride.

■ Don't use a cover of charcoal, coke, or other materials. These materials often show up in the casting as a defect. Add the zinc chloride after the metal is melted and just before you are ready to pour. Skim both before and after you add the flux.

■ Gates should be ample in size or number to fill the mold rapidly and with sufficient speed to make sure all areas of the mold are filled. You may need one small gate for a little casting or multiple gates.

■ Do not use more risers than you need. Most foundries over-riser castings and this represents waste and cost, and in many cases the riser causes a defective casting. Porosity, segregation, and shrinkage can often be eliminated with a simple chill.

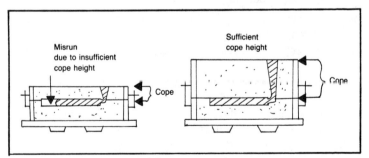

Fig. 7-52. Insufficient cope height causes a misrun.

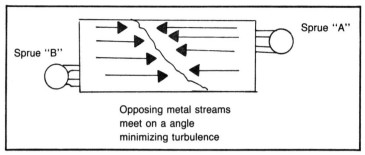

Sprue "A"

Sprue "B"

Opposing metal streams
meet on a angle
minimizing turbulence

Fig. 7-53. Stagger gates when pouring from both ends of a mold.

■ Have sufficient hydrostatic pressure. Often a casting is missed because of insufficient cope or sprue height due to the lack of sufficient hydrostatic pressure required to fill up the mold and hold up the casting. (Fig. 7-52).

■ When pouring a large or long casting with two or more ladies from opposite ends simultaneously, the opposing gates should be offset to allow the opposing streams of incoming metal to pass each other rather than to hit head on and cause turbulence and agitation. See Fig. 7-53.

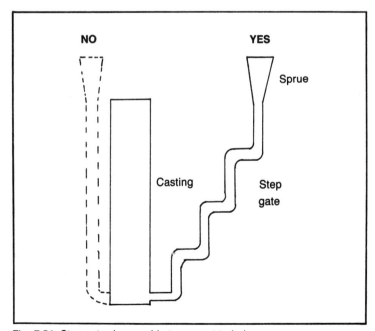

NO   YES

Sprue

Casting   Step
gate

Fig. 7-54. Step-gate deep molds to prevent turbulence.

■ Deep molds should be poured near the bottom; so step-gate deep molds to minimize turbulence and agitation. Each step arrests the flow of metal. See Fig. 7-54.

■ Don't climb a hill. In Fig. 7-55A, the metal has to crawl up the hill. When it reaches the top it spills over to the opposite leg. In Fig. 7-55B the casting is gated on the ends, and both legs of the casting fill and then meet at the top. This end-gating should also be practiced if the casting is reverse (down hill), otherwise you are pushing cold metal up hill. See Fig. 7-56.

■ When you have a large, green sand core which could cause hot tearing or excessive gassing, it should be filled with loose, sifted ashes or coke breeze (Fig. 7-57).

■ Make sure the gates are not too thin. On gating systems where no riser is used, the sprue or runner bar serves as a hot metal reservoir to feed the casting. If the gate freezes too soon (ahead of the casting), then the liquid feed metal in the sprue and/or runner bar cannot get to the casting to feed it. See Fig. 7-58.

■ Have the correct pouring height above the sprue. Pour with the ladle as close to the sprue as possible in most cases. There are exceptions to this rule, however. In some cases, in order to get sufficient velocity to run the casting, you must pour higher above the sprue, often as much as 12 inches. See Fig. 7-59.

■ When you have a gate that produces satisfactory results, leave it alone.

■ In general, most aluminum castings can be poured at the following temperatures: very light work, 3/16″, 1475 to 1500 degrees Fahrenheit; light work, 1/4″, 1300 to 1375 degrees

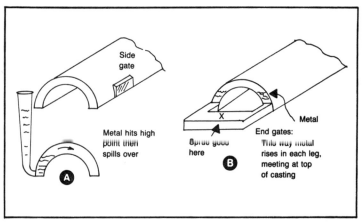

Fig. 7-55. Don't make the metal climb a hill, if possible.

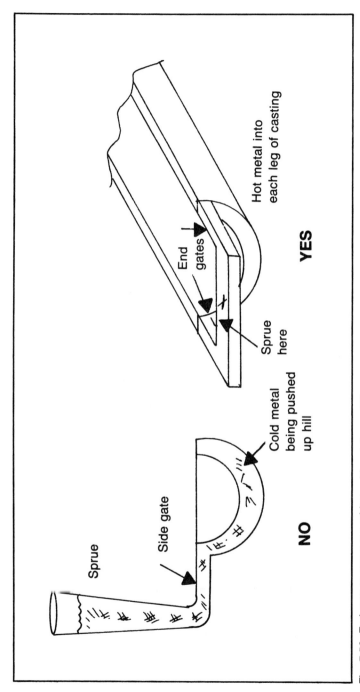

Fig. 7-56. End-gate to prevent pushing cold metal up a hill.

171

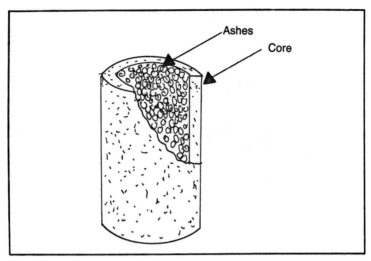

Fig. 7-57. A large core is hollowed out and filled with ashes to assist in venting.

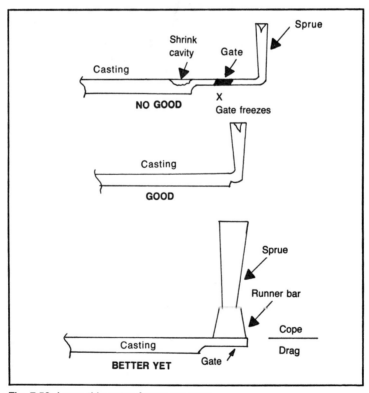

Fig. 7-58. Long, thin gates freeze too soon.

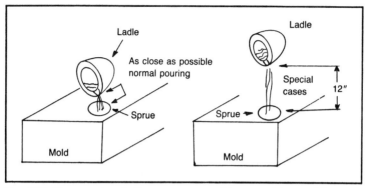

Fig. 7-59. Pour as close to the sprue as possible, except in special cases.

Fahrenheit; heavy work, 3/8″ and thicker, 1250 degrees Fahrenheit. You will find that 90 percent and more castings can be poured at close to 1400 degrees Fahrenheit. When you get above 1500 degrees Fahrenheit or below 1200 degrees Fahrenheit, you are looking for problems. There is not way you could cover a gate diagram for every conceivable type of casting. It's simply a matter of designing the gate based on the casting and using common sense.

You must fill the mold as rapidly as possible with a minimum of turbulence and agitation, provide feed metal to compensate for liquid shrinkage, and get everything to solidify toward the feed metal reservoir. The key is progressive directional solidification. In order to be effective, the solidification direction must be controlled by the careful control of the temperature gradients. See Fig. 7-60.

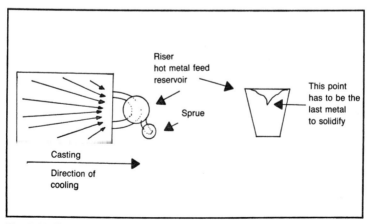

Fig. 7-60. The key is directional solidification.

8

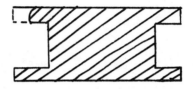

Aluminum Casting Defects

The analysis of any type of casting defect, nonferrous or ferrous, can sometimes be confusing and require one or more corrective measures. The trick is to pin it down.

To give an example, in pouring some flat 12-×-18-inch aluminum plates 1/4 inch thick, the castings came up with circular holes in various locations. The hole was not a blow, but a misrun. The metal simply chilled and did not fill in one or more areas (Fig. 8-1).

Now these holes could not have been any more perfect than if you had cored them there intentionally. It was obvious that they were misruns. The plate was gated from one long side with a runner bar and several ingates. See Fig. 8-2.

Now, why did the entire casting run all the way across to every corner and misrun in one or more areas, some even close to the ingates?

CAUSES OF MISRUNS

Let's look at the causes of misruns. Any of the following, or a combination of several, can cause a misrun.

■ Improper design. The casting is not uniform in section, causing a slowing down of the metal velocity as it fills the cavity.

■ Worn improper patterns. Thin sections are created where the pattern has worn away.

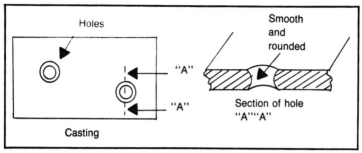

Fig. 8-1. Holes in casting are misruns.

■ Cope shift or drag shift can cause a thin section.

■ Improper mounting of patterns.

■ No tilting of the mold when pouring a flat, thin casting.

■ Insufficient number or size of gates, runners, or sprues.

■ Gates are not located in the right place.

■ Improper distribution of gates.

■ Insufficient hydrostatic pressure (height of sprue top above the top of the casting).

■ Molding sand is too wet.

■ Weak molding sand, low in green strength.

■ Cores too hard.

■ Insufficient venting.

■ Cores don't fit properly.

■ Core coating wet or too thick, reducing the metal section.

■ Sagged or raised core.

■ Core shift.

■ Uneven ramming of the cope or drag.

■ Mold rammed too hard (low permeability).

■ Mold rammed too softly.

■ Bottom board weak or not bedded properly on the drag.

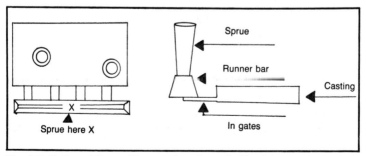

Fig. 8-2. Gating of the problem casting shown in Fig. 8-1.

175

- Excessive troweling or slicking and patching.
- Wrong size chaplet used, causing a thin section.
- Too light a chaplet is used. The chaplet is burned up too soon.
- Metal is too cold; pouring temperature is too low.
- Metal is not fluid.
- Interrupted pouring, slacking the stream, or dribbling the metal into the sprue.
- Excessive mold weights.
- Pouring pressure reduced due to a leak at the mold joint.
- Condensation in the mold cavity on thin-section work.

I could give you another ten or more causes of a misrun. A *misrun* is an incompletely fired mold cavity, where the lugs or corners are not filled out; a smoothly rounded hole through the wall of the casting, or a casting which lacks fullness or completeness because the mold cavity does not completely fill with metal; one or more of the casting's extremities is missing or only partly filled out.

A misrun can be caused by 30 or more reasons alone or in combination. So where do you start? Let's take the example in Figs. 8-1 and 8-2. We had the round, smooth hole through the wall. You can eliminate 14 causes, simply because we are casting a flat plate, with no cores, chaplets, etc. So this leaves us with 16 possibilities. Start down the line checking and changing. The only problem here is, if you change more than one thing at a time, you never know what the prime cause was when it is corrected.

You cannot make one change, pour a casting, then put the first change back like it was, make another change, and pour another casting, until you finally come up with a solution. This is impossible to do, and the cause might be from a combination of errors in practice.

Now, don't let this scare you. Most defects and their solution are usually quite obvious when you look at the scrap casting. You start with the most probable cause, which is that the pouring temperature is not high enough, and the casting simply froze before filling the cavity.

Note. A misrun is often referred to as a cold shut, but this is incorrect. A *cold shut* is a defect caused by two meeting streams of metal failing to flow together as one homogeneous body, resulting in a physical division between them. This type of defect is common with aluminum and caused primarily when the two approaching bodies of liquid metal are carrying on their leading edge an aluminum oxide coating. If the meeting streams are not hot enough and do not meet with sufficient force to break this oxide coating, they will fail to weld or melt together. See Fig. 8-3.

Misruns and cold shuts are closely related. The misrun is a discontinuity, as shown in Fig. 8-3 A, and the cold shut is a seamlike discontinuity.

The problem with this misrun turned out to be none of the 30 possible causes that I listed. The problem was that the casting was molded in a flask too small for the job. The bearing between the cope and the drag was insufficient, and the cope was sagging, causing one or more pinched-down, restricted sections. When the incoming metal got to these restricted areas, it met with this sudden increased resistance to its flow. Taking the path of least resistance, it circumvented these restricted areas. The metal at the restricted areas abruptly hesitated (decreased its flow velocity), prior to circumventing the restricted area. This slack in flow caused the defect.

It paused, circled, and froze. So the misrun was caused by a physical problem in the mold. Remember what I said about misruns in pouring practice. See Fig. 8-4.

CAUSES OF SPECIFIC DEFECTS

Improper design can cause blows, shrinks, warped castings, misruns, inclusions, expansion scabs, stickers, penetration, shifts,

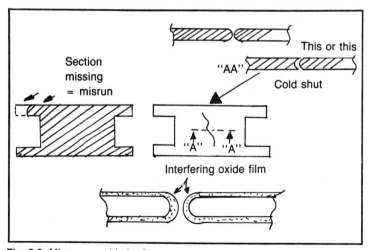

Fig. 8-3. Misrun or cold shut?

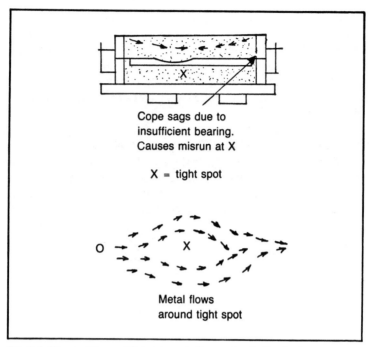

Cope sags due to
insufficient bearing.
Causes misrun at X

X = tight spot

Metal flows
around tight spot

Fig. 8-4. Cause of the problem misrun in the casting in Fig. 8-1 is insufficient bearing surface for the cope.

scabs, hot tears, open-grain structure, cold shuts, cuts and washes, drops, rough spots, swells, and core raises.

Improper pattern equipment can cause scabs, hot tears, warped castings, misruns, crushes, stickers, penetration, shifts, ramoffs, run outs, shrinkage, cracks, open-grain structure, cold shuts, drops, rough surfaces, swells, core raises, cores wrong, and bleeders.

Faulty flask and rigging can cause blows, shrinks, cracks, misruns, scabs, crushes, penetration, shifts, cores wrong, hot tears, warped castings, cold shuts, erosion, drops, rough surfaces, swells, ramoffs, and run outs.

Gates and risers can cause blows, shrinks, warped castings, misruns, inclusions, scabs, stickers, penetration, core raises, run outs, hot tears, open-grain structures, cold shuts, cuts and washes, drops, rough surfaces, swells, ram offs and bleeders.

Molding sand can cause blows, hot tears, warped castings, cold shuts, cuts and washes, crushes, stickers, penetration, core raises, run outs, cracks, misruns, inclusions, scabs, drops, rough surfaces, swells, ramoffs, and bleeders.

Cores can cause blows, hot tears, warped castings, inclusions, erosion scabs, crushes, penetration, shifts, cores, wrong, scabs, cracks, misruns, cuts and washes, stickers, rough surfaces, swells, core raises, run outs, and bleeders.

Molding practice can cause blows, hot tears, warped castings, misruns, inclusions, erosion, drops, rough surfaces, swells, core raises, runouts, scabs, cracks, open-grain structures, cold shuts, cuts and washes, crushes, stickers, penetration, shifts, ramoffs, and bleeders.

Metal composition can be responsible for blows, shrinks, cracks, open-grain structures, cold shuts, penetration, scabs, hot tears, warped castings, misruns, and rough surfaces.

Melting practice can cause blows, hot tears, warped castings, misruns, inclusions, shrinks, cracks, open-grain structures, and cold shuts.

Pouring can cause blows, shrinks, cracks, open-grain structures, cold shuts, scabs, drops, penetration, swells, core raises, bleeders, poured short, scars and plates, hot tears, warped castings, misruns, inclusions, crushes, rough surfaces, fusion, shifts, run outs, and broken castings.

As you see, you can cause quite a few problems simply by not pouring the casting correctly.

Of course, other problems are common only to a particular metal, such as kish, which is a cast-iron defect, or zinc worms, a problem with high zinc-copper-based alloys. Let's take the basic ten casting defects, which cover 99 percent of the defects you could have with aluminum, and look at these a little closer.

TEN MOST COMMON ALUMINUM CASTING DEFECTS

Shrinkage cracks and cavities (hot tearing). Definition: Cracks or cavities from the metal pulling itself apart while cooling in the mold. Primary Causes: Light and heavy sections (abrupt section change); lack of fillets (poor design); insufficient gating temperature to run the casting; inadequate risers for feeding; pouring temperature too high or too low; excessive hot strength of molding sand.

Cold shut. Definition: The lack of joining where two streams of metal meet, leaving a crack or weak spot. Primary Causes: Insufficient pouring head (cope too shallow, sprue too short, lacks hydrostatic pressure); insufficient number of gates or a restriction in a gate or sprue preventing the metal from filling the mold fast enough; insufficient venting; sand too wet; permeability of the sand too low; metal sluggish due to badly gassed melt; poor melting practice which will give you the badly gassed, sluggish metal and metal full of oxides; metal too cold (pouring temperature too low); improper or incomplete skimming, which could allow dross to be poured into the sprue blocking it and restricting the metal flow; pouring too slow, bobbling, or slacking the stream during pouring; stop pouring too soon.

Sand wash. Definition: Rough lumps of metal (containing sand) at some points on the casting and rough sandy holes at other points. Primary Causes: Rough surface on pattern or a pattern with insufficient draft, causing weakening of the sand when the pattern is drawn from the mold; weak areas around the gate or sharp corners at the gates; mold not rammed hard enough; weak, poorly bonded sand; overcooked (burnt) core; core crush.

Scab. Definition: A slightly raised surface on the casting with sand under this raised section. This defect, when removed, leaves you with a new defect called a *buckle*. Primary Causes: Hard ramming; sand too fine and permeability too low; sand lacks combustibles, i.e. wood flour.

Core blow. Definition: A smooth depression on the inner surface of a cored casting or a gas pocket above the cored cavity. Primary causes: Insufficient core print or adequate core vent; core not baked completely; hot core set in cold mold, causing condensation to form on core surface; dry sand core left in green sand mold too long before pouring, allowing the core to absorb moisture from the moist molding sand.

Penetration (burn in). Definition: Rough sandy appearance of the outer surface of the casting, this rough surface containing a mixture of metal and sand. Primary Causes: Sand too coarse for the job (too open); the permeability too high; metal excessively fluid; excessive pouring temperature.

Weak or discontinuous structure (often called shrinkage porosity). Definition: Cavities or voids between rather large metal crystals. Casting has a weak porous structure at the defect sight. The fracture is coarse and granular in appearance. Primary Causes: Heavy sections adjoining light sections; heavy sections which are isolated and hard to feed during solidification.

Core metal penetration. Definition: A rough surface on a casting in a cored cavity or section, including sand mixed with metal. Metal fins which penetrate the core also include sand. Primary Causes: Cores which have been overbaked (destroying the

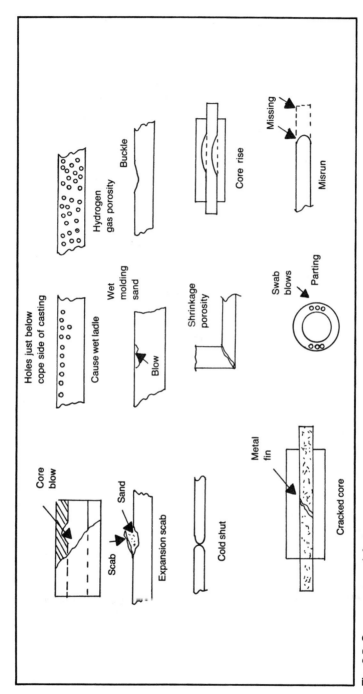

Fig. 8-5. Some common defects.

binder, burned cores); core mix improper, insufficient binder, wrong binder; core mix not mixed properly to distribute the binder properly and coat each rain of sand; core sand too coarse and open; excessive pouring temperature.

Gas holes. Definition: Holes under or near the surface of the casting, which, when sectioned, present a round, untarnished appearance. This is quite different from gas porosity (hydrogen absorption, which is fine round voids throughout the entire casting). Primary Causes: Inadequate fillets; excessively thin sections which require 1500 degrees Fahrenheit plus pouring temperature; molding sand too wet; too much new molding sand in the system sand; underbaked or poorly vented cores; pouring temperature too high.

Misrun. Definition: An incompletely filled mold cavity. Lugs, corners, etc., not filled out, or a smoothly rounded hole through a casting wall. Primary Causes: Insufficient sprue height; gate too small, or choked too tight; insufficient gates; inadequate venting; sand too wet; permeability too low; sand too wet; permeability too low; metal too gassy with hydrogen making it sluggish; interrupted pouring; too slow pouring; metal not hot enough.

A misrun caused by pouring the mold short (not enough metal in the ladle) is simply a defect that you don't need. A misrun due to metal leaking out between the cope and drag or a cracked cope or drag is still a misrun but is called a *run out.*

As you will note, I have given 10 primary causes for a misrun here, but earlier I showed 30 things that can cause a misrun. Study the 30 closely, and you will realize that there is no excuse for misrunning a casting in most of these ways. More castings are probably lost to misruns than any other defect, and it is usually boiled down to pouring, cold metal, trying to pour too many molds from a single ladle or crucible, the last mold getting cold metal, or pouring short. If you intend to pour several different molds from a single ladleful, arrange them so that the thin work gets the first metal, and the heavy jobs get the last. See Fig. 8-5.

Good, sound, basic practice with attention to all the details, regardless of how minor they might seem, will keep your scrap at a minimum. When you have a defective casting, the key is to be able to identify the cause correctly. You must pin down the causes, and as you see, all defects can be the product of one of many things going wrong.

9

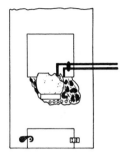

Heat Treatment

Binary aluminum alloys which contain 6 percent magnesium respond to heat treatment, as do alloys containing silicon and magnesium. The silicon and the magnesium form the compound magnesium silicide, which increases the strength and hardness but reduces the ductility of the alloy. With these alloys, maximum results are obtained by heat-treating the castings. *Heat treatment* is the process in which a casting is heated and then cooled under controlled conditions.

PURPOSES

The purposes of heat treatment are to:

■ Develop a uniform structure throughout the casting.

■ Remove internal stresses caused by the thermal conditions or contraction during solidification. This treatment is often referred to as *stress relief*. It is used on a casting that is uptight as cast, and that you wish to get to relax.

■ Improve the mechanical properties, such as strength and elongation.

■ Improve dimensional stability. Of course if you can get the casting to the point where the various constituents in the alloy are distributed evenly throughout the casting and get the casting to relax, you automatically accomplish the second and third purposes.

DIMENSIONAL STABILITY

You cannot mix up the constituents of a casting and get them evenly distributed throughout the castings. When the casting is liquid, however, all the various constituents, the molecules of aluminum, silicon, magnesium, etc., are evenly distributed throughout it.

It's when the casting goes from a liquid state to a solid that the problem starts. As the molten aluminum alloy solidifies, various crystal aggregates precipitate from the molten metal. Segregation takes place. The size, shape, nature, and location of these various crystals depend upon many things.

Cooling Rate

If you could simply cause the casting to freeze, or solidify, the instant the mold is filled, everything would be stopped in its track with no chance for any segregation. So the segregation problem involves the cooling rate of the casting. Now, most castings are composed of sections of various thicknesses. This characteristic produces, or can produce, a considerable difference in the structure because of the different cooling rates of these sections.

Because of this difference in the cooling rate, the constituents that remain in solution will vary in amount among sections. In a thin section, which solidifies rapidly, more of the constituents will remain in solution than in a thick section. We are talking about solid solution.

Solid Solution. *Solid solution* is defined as a solid, homogeneous mixture of two or more substances. For example, some alloys are solid solutions of the metals in each other, the process of solution having taken place in the molten state. Therefore, you must maintain this solution which took place in the molten state (by dissolving one or more metals together through melting them together) in the solid state. Now, because you cannot simply cause the metal to freeze fast enough to prevent segregation, you must take a different approach.

Coring. This segregation problem is called *coring*. It is the segregation of low and high-melting compositions, and is often called *dendritic segregation*. This dendritic segregation is usually caused by very slow or too slow cooling from a liquid to a solid, upsetting the equilibrium conditions. See Fig. 9-1.

The reason metal alloy solutions segregate during solidification is that the first portions to solidify (freeze) are the highest

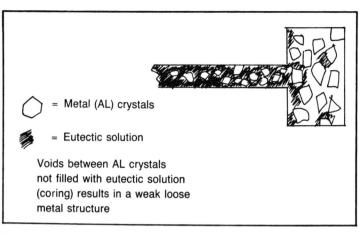

Fig. 9-1. Coring is illustrated.

```
        = Metal (AL) crystals

        = Eutectic solution

     Voids between AL crystals
     not filled with eutectic solution
     (coring) results in a weak loose
     metal structure
```

melting constituent then the next-highest melting constituent, etc. This selective freezing of each constituent, each with different melting and freezing temperatures, results in the uneven concentration of the elements that make up the alloy.

Eutectic

The eutectic mixture is a solid solution of two or more substances having the lowest freezing point of all the possible mixtures of components. The *eutectic point*, then, would be the minimum freezing point attainable corresponding to the eutectic mixture. A solid solution of aluminum and copper melted together has a lower melting temperature than pure aluminum or pure copper. If you vary the percentages of aluminum to copper or copper to aluminum, you will find that there is one combination that will have the lowest melting point of all combinations. This would be the eutectic point and the eutectic mixture. This point or percent mixture is governed by the solubility of one constituent in another.

In metals you are dealing with solubility at room temperature. The compound I spoke about, magnesium silicide, is an example. It is soluble up to 1.85 percent at 1103 degrees Fahrenheit in aluminum, but is soluble less than .25 percent at room temperature.

Solution Treating

Fortunately, the various constituents of the alloy have different melting and freezing temperatures, and atomic mobility is increased

185

with temperature. All you have to do, therefore, is to heat the casting up to the point just below its solution temperature. When you do this you are redissolving these lower melting constituents. This dissolving, for the most part, is accompanied with a greatly increased atomic mobility. The solution temperature for aluminum alloys is from 820 to 1000 degrees Fahrenheit. This varies with the chemical composition of the alloy. If the solution-treatment temperature is too high, you can warp the casting or, at the worst, melt it.

When the precipitated constituents are redissolved and active (moving about due to atomic mobility), they redistribute themselves throughout the casting evenly, producing the same homogeneous mixture you had when the metal was a liquid in the crucible or mold.

This mixture is not accomplished instantly when you reach the solution temperature of a particular alloy. The atoms must have time to make the trip, taking into account the rate or speed of diffusion and the distance which the atoms must travel. The length of time will vary with each solid solution. Generally speaking, the time required at the solution temperature (soaking time) is from 12 to 15 hours to produce a complete redistribution. The casting size and thickness also have a bearing on the length of time. A coarser-grained structure requires a longer solution-treating time than one of a finer grain. When you reach the proper soaking time, anything longer is a waste of time and energy. I will give you some typical times for various alloys; however, because each casting differs, you must determine what is best for each individual casting.

Quenching

Now you have the desired metallic structure changes. That is, the atoms have rearranged themselves to produce the correct complete distribution throughout the casting.

If you let the casting simply cool back down to room temperature, you are back where you started; everything will reprecipitate. What you must do, then, is get the castings out of the heat treating oven as fast as possible and cool them off as quickly as you can. This chilling, or *quenching*, stops everything in its tracks, locking all the constituents in place.

The quickest way to quench is to pull the hot castings and dump them in ice water. This method would be so severe that the shock would cause the casting to distort or crack like a hot piece of glass dumped into cold water. The usual procedure is to quench the castings in boiling or near-boiling water. The move from solution temperature to the hot water must, as I pointed out, be done quickly. You want to retain the homogeneous structure you accomplished by the redissolving treatment.

In some alloys, the reprecipitation is so slow and sluggish that it is not necessary to quench or cool the castings by dumping them in boiling water. These alloys can be removed from the heat-treating oven and simply allowed to air cool.

Natural Aging Treatment. When you solution-treat the casting and then quench, you have a casting in which the alloy is unstable. The strength is higher than the as-cast condition, and usually the casting is considerably more ductile.

Changes begin to take place internally at room temperature— a natural self-adjustment of the constituents to the unstable condition caused by heating and quenching. This structural change starts rather soon, and within 24 hours after quenching, the ductility is reduced. So, if you wish to bend or straighten a casting, you should do so shortly after the casting reaches room temperature from the quench bath, otherwise you could run into problems. The natural aging treatment allows the casting, after quenching, to simply lay around at room temperature for a period of time, 24 hours, or so, prior to a stress-relieving treatment.

Artificial Aging. The results of artificial aging are identical to the natural aging treatment. It is only a time-saving move. What it amounts to is simply heating the casting up to about 300 degrees Fahrenheit, holding it at this temperature for a period of time, then allowing the casting to cool naturally to room temperature.

Stress Relief

Stress relief is simply what the name says, and does not have much bearing on the physical properties of the casting. The mechanical properties, such as tensile strength, elongation, hardness, etc., remain about the same as the as-cast properties of the casting. Stress relief simply removes any internal stresses set up in the casting due to the various cooling rates of the different section thicknesses during solidification. It's a relaxing treatment. What little physical changes take place are minor.

The general procedure is to heat the castings up to somewhere in the range of 450 to 650 degrees Fahrenheit, hold them at the selected temperature for a period of time and then let the casting naturally cool to room temperature.

THE HEAT-TREAT FURNACE

In order to do effective heat treating, you must have a furnace which can be precisely temperature-controlled. That is, it must be equipped with good, accurate, automatic temperature-control instruments. You want a temperature control that will keep the selected temperature to within plus or minus 5 degrees Fahrenheit. You should have, not one, but several, thermocouples placed in different locations in the furnace. All should be equipped with a fail-safe alarm should the temperature decide, due to a malfunction, to climb past the set limit. Remember, a solution treatment can be very close to the melting temperature of the casting. A miss here could result in a melted or partially melted casting.

Recording pyrometers are the best thermocouples to use. You want an air-chamber furnace heated by electric heating units, such as chromalox units or hot rods. Gas- or oil-fired ovens are also used; however, electric is easier to control and much cleaner.

With a gas- or oil-fired furnace where the products of combustion are circulated, you must be sure that these products of combustion are clean of moisture, sulphur, and carbon dioxide. A good bet for the small shop is an electric top-loading potter's kiln with the necessary temperature controls.

The quench bath can be heated by stream, electricity, gas, or oil. The casting must be arranged in the baskets or racks so that there is sufficient space around each casting for free heat circulation. Baffles may be required in the furnace to prevent direct radiation and to prevent air from being drawn directly from the heating units onto the castings.

Not many small aluminum foundries have any heat-treating equipment, but shop this end of the work out to a commercial heat-treating firm. It is quite a business in its own right. It is also customary for a large foundry with a heat-treat department to take in outside work from the surrounding smaller firms to help the heat-treat department pay its way.

I worked for a very large foundry once that did so much outside job heat treating that it became a major portion of their income. For a small foundry faced with occasional heat-treat requirements, you will often find that a small setup to do your own heat treating even just now and then will pay off. Outside heat treatment can be very costly, especially if you must ship the castings back and forth any distance. At any rate, even the smallest backyard hobby caster should know at least the basic fundamentals of heat treating.

Some Sandcast Alloys and Recommended Heat Treatments

There are considerable aluminum alloys that will respond to different types of precipitation hardening. These alloys are basically combinations of: aluminum-copper-manganese, aluminum-copper-manganese-silicon, aluminum-copper-magnesium-nickel, aluminum-magnesium-silicide, and aluminum-magnesium-zincide. The two compounds magnesium silicide and magnesium zincide are binary compounds formed up in the alloy.

There are six methods of heat treatment. They are: T1 = Naturally aged; T2 = Annealed; T4 = Solution heat treated; T5 = Artificially Aged only (stress relieved); T6 = Solution heat treated, then artificially aged; and T7 = Solution heat treated, then stabilized. The whole number designates the specific conditions of the heat treat for the particular alloy involved.

Let's look at a typical specification. The print calls for the casting to be made out of alloy 356T4; so we make the casting out of the commercial alloy #356 consisting of 92.7 percent aluminum, 7 percent silicon, and 0.3 percent magnesium, and then we give it a T4 heat treatment, which is a solution heat treat. The suggested practice for a T4 heat treatment for alloy #356 is to soak the casting at 1000 degrees Fahrenheit for 6 to 24 hours and then quench in boiling or near-boiling water.

Some alloys can be given various types of heat treating for various characteristics. You might see a specification calling for 356T5 or 356T51. In this case, both specifications call for T5, which is a stress-relieving treatment, and one also calls for T1, which is artificial aging.

Pure aluminum does not respond to heat treating; however when it is work hardened, such as through drawing wire, hammering, or repeated bending, it can be *annealed*, or softened, by heating to a temperature slightly in excess of 650 degrees Fahrenheit and cooling to room temperature. There is no need to soak the aluminum at a higher temperature because the annealing is almost instantaneous as long as the annealing temperature exceeds the recrystallization temperature of the aluminum. At this temperature, the strain-hardened crystals simply recrystallize into new, relaxed, soft grains.

Alloys that will respond to heat treating have the suffix T added to the alloy identification number; 356T is an alloy consisting of 7 percent silicon, 0.3 percent magnesium, and 92.7 percent aluminum. The first digit following the T indicates the general type of heat treatment.

In both specifications of the example we have been discussing, the first digit after the T is 5, but one specification has an additional digit after the 5. Both 356T5 and 356T51 are going to be stress relieved, but the practice is going to be different. A T5 stress-relieving practice for 356 consists of heating the casting to 450 degrees Fahrenheit for 4 to 5 hours and letting it cool to room temperature. A T51 stress relieving treatment consists of heating the casting to 440 degrees Fahrenheit for 7 to 9 hours and allowing it to cool to room temperature. A T5 or T51 stress-relieving treatment has no effect on the mechanical properties of an alloy; they would only relax the casting. It would have the same properties as it would in the as-cast condition without stress relieving.

Let's look at the mechanical property changes by giving the same alloy different heat treatments.

Alloy 356 as-cast: Tensile strength, 23,000 pounds per square inch; elongation 2 percent in 2 inches; brinell hardness, 60. With T5 or T51 heat treatment, it is the same as the as-cast.

Alloy 356T6: Tensile strength, 30,000 pounds per square inch; elongation 4 percent in 2 inches; brinell hardness, 70.

Alloy 356T7: Tensile strength, 31,000 pounds per square inch; elongation 2 percent in 2 inches; brinell hardness, 75.

Alloy 356T71: Tensile strength, 25,000 pounds per square inch; elongation, 4.5 percent in 2 inches; brinell hardness, 60.

The brinell hardness was a 10-millimeter ball at a 500-kilogram load.

As you can see, with various heat treatments you can accomplish quite a few different physical property changes for a given alloy.

From a tensile strength of 23,000 as-cast, the 356 alloy jumps to 31,000, which is a net gain of 8,000 pounds per square inch more strength by simply subjecting the casting to a T7 heat treat.

General Suggested Heat-Treating Practices

Each alloy can be identified by many different identifying numbers; i.e. 356 is the former commercial designation for the alloy made of 92.7 percent aluminum, 7 percent silicon, and 0.5 percent magnesium. AA calls it 356.1. ASTM calls it SG70A-SG70C. SAE calls it 323. The federal government calls it QQ-A 371 E 356, and each ingot maker has its own designation. I am going to stick with the old numbers. If you ask for it by the number I give, your supplier will cross-index it to his number.

Alloy #122. Treatment: T2, heat at 600 degrees Fahrenheit

190

for 2 to 4 hours and air cool. Treatment: T61, heat at 950 degrees Fahrenheit for 12 hours, quench in hot water then reheat to 310 degrees Fahrenheit for 10 to 12 hours and air cool.

Alloy #142. Treatment: T21, heat at 650 degrees Fahrenheit for 2 to 4 hours and air cool. Treatment: T77, heat at 970 degrees Fahrenheit for 6 hours, air cool in still air then reheat to 650 degrees Fahrenheit for 1 to 3 hours and air cool.

Alloy #195. Treatment: T4, heat at 960 degrees Fahrenheit for 12 hours and quench in hot water. Treatment: T6, heat at 960 degrees Fahrenheit for 12 hours and quench in hot water then reheat to 310 degrees Fahrenheit for 3 to 5 hours and air cool. Treatment: T62, heat at 960 degrees Fahrenheit for 12 hours and quench in hot water then reheat at 310 degees Fahrenheit for 12 to 16 hours and air cool.

Alloy #319. Treatment: T6, heat at 940 degrees Fahrenheit for 12 hours and quench in hot water, then reheat to 310 degrees Fahrenheit for 2 to 5 hours and air cool.

Alloy #355. Treatment: T51, heat to 440 degrees Fahrenheit for 7 to 9 hours and air cool. Treatment: T6, heat to 980 degrees Fahrenheit for 12 hours and quench in hot water then reheat to 310 degrees Fahrenheit for 3 to 5 hours and air cool. Treatment: T61, heat to 980 degrees Fahrenheit for 12 hours and quench in hot water then reheat to 310 degrees Fahrenheit for 8 to 10 hours and air cool. Treatment: T7, heat to 980 degrees Fahrenheit for 12 hours and quench in hot water then reheat to 440 degrees Fahrenheit for 7 to 9 hours and air cool. Treatment: T71, heat to 980 degrees Fahrenheit for 12 hours and quench in hot water then reheat to 475 degrees Fahrenheit for 4 to 6 hours and air cool.

Note: 355 will respond to 5 different types of heat treatment.

Alloy #356. Treatment: T51, heat at 440 degrees Fahrenheit for 7 to 9 hours and air cool. Treatment: T6 heat at 1000 degrees Fahrenheit for 12 hours, quench in hot water then reheat to 310 degrees Fahrenheit for 2 to 5 hours and air cool. Treatment: T7, heat to 1000 degrees Fahrenheit for 12 hours and quench in hot water then reheat to 440 degrees Fahrenheit for 7 to 9 hours and air cool. Treatment: T71, heat to 1000 degrees Fahrenheit for 12 hours and quench in hot water then reheat to 475 degrees Fahrenheit for 2 to 4 hours and air cool.

You will note that the high soaking temperatures of 940 to 1000 degrees Fahrenheit represent the temperature where a particular alloy will redissolve (redistribute the constituents) which have segregated during casting. The lower temperatures of 310 to 600 degrees Fahrenheit are the temperatures of adjustment. The times given are approximate due to the wide differences you could have in casting weights, configuration, etc. Your quench water should be boiling if possible to minimize problems with stresses and distortion; however you can go as low as 150 degrees Fahrenheit on your water temperature at sea level. Where I live, at 6,000 feet above sea level, water even at boiling is not very hot.

If the casting is cast in a permanent cast-iron or graphite mold, there is far less segregation because of the chilling effect of the mold, which arrests the precipitation for the most part. Remember, the slower a casting cools in the mold, the more problem you will have with segregation, large grain growth, etc.

If you cast alloy #356 in a cast-iron permold, the T6 heat treatment would only be 8 hours of soaking at 1000 degrees Fahrenheit in place of 12 hours because fewer constituents must be redissolved and return to their proper place. The atoms have less distance to travel.

THE HEAT-TREATING DECISION

The decision whether or not to heat treat depends on where the monkey's tail is. If you are casting a coat hook to hang up your coat, you would choose the cheapest alloy you could buy, which would be alloy #112—a simple alloy of 91.3 percent aluminum, 7 percent copper, and 1.7 percent zinc or simply scrap pistons, etc. You would not choose a more expensive heat-treatable alloy such as #356. If the casting is going to be subjected to extensive machining, stress pressure, etc., then you would look for the alloy that would, by heat treating, give you the required characteristics needed in the end product.

Select the proper foundry practice and heat treatment and jump on it. I have seen homemade equipment, machinery, gears, etc., made in the hobby foundry and home machine shop from all scrap aluminum or 112 ingot with no thought whatsoever to the physical requirements of the finished item or items. Before long the castings failed, warped, were too soft, etc., so it was a big waste of time and effort. Now, it might not matter if you are making castings for your own amazement, however, if you are jobbing casting, you can wind up with a product liability suit, because one of your castings failed in service.

One time my company bid on a job to make hundreds of 4-foot diameter, 6-bladed cast-aluminum industrial fans. We lost the job

192

to a competitor by the cost we had figured in for heat treating the fans. Well, to make a long story short, when the fans made by our competition started to come apart and crack, we were offered the job at our price and made them for years with no problems.

If you ever need to make a casting that has to be machined to a very smooth, mirror finish you simply must have a good, hard casting. If you cannot heat treat it to the proper hardness you cannot do the job.

Of course you will, if you job, get some ridiculous specifications. You simply try to educate these people or send them packing. The point is you should consider heat treating.

10

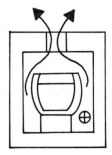

Aluminum Alloys

There are countless alloys available and new ones springing up all the time. It would be impractical for a small foundry to carry even a dozen different alloys. Over the years, as a new alloy is developed, in most cases, other than a special-application alloy, it usually replaces one or more of the older alloys. The new allow has better casting characteristics and physical properties. The older alloys will, however, hang around for years, as long as the smelters have enough call for them to justify producing them.

Don't be surprised if an alloy mentioned here is no longer available. Your best bet for a small shop, if you are doing jobbing work, is to carry one ingot for general run-of-the-mill castings where the castings do not have any particular qualifications. i.e. One ingot that can be given a number of different physical properties by various heat treatments and is also fairly easy to cast is #356. Another is a self-aging, high strength alloy requiring no heat treatment, called Federated Metals' Tenzaloy.

Some good, selected cast-aluminum scrap is always handy. When you get a customer who had decided that he wants an alloy other than the one you normally can provide, make him pay up front for this metal and keep his alloy and the return gates and risers separate for his work. Avoid the job if you cannot sell him on something you can provide from your stock. Another way to handle this situation is to charge a high premium to stock and cast with uncommon or special alloys. Of course, if you are captive and produce a product, the metal supply becomes quite simple.

MASTER ALLOYS

As I have already explained, master alloys are alloys used to produce ingots (alloys) of the desired specification from pure aluminum, or to adjust and alter a heat of an alloy scrap or ingots to a new desired specification. Beer cans are more or less pure aluminum. If you cannot purchase scrap cast aluminum at the right price, you can consider using cans and a 50/50 silicon master alloy to give you a good, general-purpose casting alloy, such as ingot #43 which is 95 percent aluminum and 5 percent silicon. You can run an ad in the paper offering a cent or two per pound above what the collection centers or the junkyards pay, and come up with a year's supply of cans quickly.

The percentages shown in Table 10-1 are the added metal, such as silicon, iron, or boron. The remainder of the master alloy is pure aluminum. Therefore the boron-aluminum master alloy is available in two different grades, one of which is 3 percent boron and 97 percent aluminum. The other grade is 4 percent boron and 96 percent aluminum. You will notice that the most-used master alloys are offered in a wider grade selection. (Manganese is available in six grades.) There is no aluminum-magnesium master alloy. Magnesium can be purchased as ingot.

Pure Aluminum

Aluminum is only available in a 50-pound ingot in 5 grades of purity—99 percent pure, 99.75 percent pure, 99.8 percent pure, 99.85 percent pure, and 99.9 percent pure.

Table 10-1. Percentages of Added Metals.

Aluminum Master Alloys Available
Boron-aluminum: 3% or 4%
Chromium-aluminum: 10% or 20%
Copper-aluminum: Various percents.
Manganese-aluminum: 5%, 7%, 10%, 20%, 25% and 30%.
Molydbenum-aluminum: 60% Al 40% Mo.
Nickel-aluminum: 20%.
Silicon-aluminum: 50%.
Titanium-aluminum: 6% or 10%.
Titanium-boron-aluminum: 5%Ti
Vanadium-aluminum: 2.5%, 5%, 10%, 40% and 85%.
Zirconium-aluminum: 3% and 6%.
Aluminum-silicon-iron: Al 20%, Si 40%, Fe 40%.
Ferro-aluminum: 35% or 40%.

Aluminum-Copper Alloys

Alloy #122. 89.8 percent aluminum, 10 percent copper, and .2 percent magnesium. It is a good sand-casting alloy for a wide variety of uses, such as air-cooled cylinder heads, bearings, bearing caps, bushings, etc. It can be heat treated, and it will retain its strength well at elevated temperatures. It machines well and has good hardness. A T61 heat treat will give it a tensile strength of 30,000 PSI and a brinell hardness of 115.

Alloy #195. 95.5 percent aluminum and 4.5 percent copper. This alloy is easy to make out of beer cans by adding copper clippings. It is a fairly good sand-casting alloy, but it has high shrinkage. The mechanical properties are good, and it machines well. It is good for rugged castings, such as crank cases, housings, wheels, and axle housings.

Alloy #112. 91.3 percent aluminum, 7.0 percent copper, and 1.7 percent zinc. This alloy is an old-timer still available for casting. It casts very easily in sand or a permanent mold, and is easy to machine. It is a fine, cheap, general casting alloy and can be used for manifolds, cover plates, electric boxes, handles, etc. The tensile strength is about 19,000 PSI as-cast, with a brinell hardness of 70.

Alloy #113. 89.3 percent aluminum, 7 percent copper, 2.0 percent silicon, and 1.7 percent zinc. This alloy is the same as 112, with the exception that it has the 2 percent silicon. It was no doubt designed to replace alloy #112. The modification results in better pressure tightness, a denser grain structure, less shrinkage, and a more fluid pouring metal. It's general use is the same as #112 and it can also be cast in permanent molds. The tensile strength as-cast is the same as #112, as is the hardness.

Another alloy which is a modification of 112 is called C113. It is 89.5 percent aluminum, 7 percent copper, and 3.5 percent silicon. In this case, the zinc has been eliminated and the silicon percent increased.

A further modification of alloy 112 is called alloy 212. It is 89.8 percent aluminum, 8 percent copper, 1 percent iron, and 1.2 percent silicon. This alloy has the same tensile strength as #112 (19,000 PSI) with a brinell hardness of 65; so it is a shade softer. It has greatly improved foundry characteristics over 112, however, and is less hot short; so you will have less hot tearing problems. The general uses are the same as 112.

Aluminum-Silicon Alloys

Alloy #43. 95 percent aluminum and 5 percent silicon. It is a good alloy for sand casting and permanent mold casting with good foundry characteristics, pressure tightness, weldability, and very good resistance to corrosion. It is great for cooking utensils, food-handling equipment, pipe fittings, and ornamental work. This alloy can also be die cast (cold chamber) to produce cookware and general-purpose castings.

A much-used silicon alloy, known as alloy #13 or A13, is 88 percent aluminum and 12 percent silicon. The only difference between the two is that A13 has less impurities, especially iron. They are not considered sand-casting nor permanent-mold alloys, but are used in die casting.

Aluminum-Copper-Silicon Alloys

Alloy #85. 81 percent aluminum, 4 percent copper, and 5 percent silicon. It is a good, strong, ductile, die-casting alloy, especially good in thick sections. Typical strength as die cast is 40,000 PSI. It is fine for levers, gears, frames, housings, etc.

Alloy #108. 93 percent aluminum, 4 percent copper, and 3 percent silicon. It is a good sand-casting alloy for pressure tightness, better than an aluminum-copper alloy, and used for a wide variety of work, such as manifolds, valve bodies, pipe fittings, etc. It has a tensile strength of 19,000 PSI, with a brinell hardness of 55.

A modification of this alloy is called A108. It is 90 percent aluminum, 4.5 percent copper, and 5.5 percent silicon. The modification is for permanent mold casting of such items as automobile grills, ornamental grills, reflectors, and castings requiring pressure tightness with moderate strength and easy weldability.

Alloy #138. 85.8 percent aluminum, 10 percent copper, 4 percent silicon, and 0.2 percent magnesium. It is basically a permanent-mold-casting alloy where you want a hard casting. The brinell hardness is 100 as-cast, with a tensile strength of 26,000 PSI. This alloy was originally developed for casting sole plates for electric hand irons where the electric element was cast into the sole plate. It is also used for electric fry pans and things of this nature cast in a permanent mold. This alloy will take a fine, smooth finish that resists scratching.

Alloy #152. 87.2 percent aluminum, 7 percent copper, 5.5

percent silicon, and 0.3 percent magnesium. This alloy is an old and much-used alloy for casting pistons in permanent molds. It has good casting characteristics and machinability. The castings can be artificially aged (152T524) or solution heat-treated and artificially aged (152T74). The T74 is the usual way to go. The typical T74 treatment for this alloy is heat to 920 degrees Fahrenheit for 8 hours, quench in boiling water, then age at 525 degrees Fahrenheit for 2 to 4 hours and air cool. This process should result in a minimum tensile strength of 30,000 PSI. With only the T524 treatment, the tensile strength is 27,000 PSI, with a brinell hardness of 95 to 100.

Alloy #319. 91 percent aluminum, 3 percent copper and 6 percent silicon. It is a good, all-around alloy for sand or permanent mold casting.

It can be 319T6 heat treated for a minimum tensile strength of 31,000 PSI and a brinell hardness of 80 as-cast. With no heat treatment, it is about 23,000 PSI with a brinell of 70.

Alloy #333. 83.2 percent aluminum, 3.8 percent copper, 9 percent silicon, and 0.4 percent magnesium. This alloy has a very low coefficient of thermal expansion and is very suitable for castings subjected to high temperature, such as pistons and iron soles. Motorcycle air-cooled engine pistons operate at a higher temperature than liquid-cooled engines. Heat treated (333T533), the tensile strength is 30,000 PSI with a brinell of 100. Sometimes alloy #333 is formulated as 87 percent aluminum, 3.5 percent copper, and 9.5 percent silicon, without the .4 percent magnesium; it is not as good an alloy.

Aluminum-Silicon-Magnesium Alloys

Alloy #355. 93.2 percent aluminum, 5 percent silicon, and 1.3 percent copper. This is a good, all-around, heat-treatable alloy, suitable for sand or permanent molds. It has excellent casting characteristics, pressure tightness, weldability, and machinability. This alloy is used for aircraft castings, fuel pump bodies, gears, cylinder heads, pump and supercharge impellers, etc. It will respond to a number of types of heat treatment. A permanent mold casting of 355 with a T62 designation consists of a solution heat treatment at 980 degrees Fahrenheit for 8 hours and a quenching in boiling water, then artificial aging at 340 degrees Fahrenheit for 14 to 18 hours. The cast will have a tensile strength of approximately 42,000 PSI or greater, with a brinell hardness of 105. A 355T61 sand casting will have a tensile strength of 36,000 PSI and a brinell hardness of 90.

Alloy #356. 92.5 percent aluminum, 7 percent silicon, and 0.5 percent magnesium. It is a good alloy for pump parts, wheels, gears, machine parts etc., that are cast in sand or permanent molds. An excellent foundry metal, it has good pressure tightness and corrosive resistance, and it is heat-treatable.

I can remember the time when almost everything we sand-cast in aluminum called for 356T6. The T6 heat treatment was a solution heat treat at 1000 degrees Fahrenheit for 12 hours, a quenching in boiling water, followed by an aging treatment at 310 degrees Fahrenheit for 2 to 5 hours. The treatment gave the casting these approximate mechanical properties: tensile strength, 30,000 PSI; elongation percent in 2 inches, 3 percent yield strength, 24,000 PSI; ultimate strength, 33,000 PSI; brinell hardness, 70; shear strength, 27,000 PSI; and fatigue, 8,000 PSI.

Well, when you look at these figures it is easy to see how versatile this alloy could be for countless uses. It is still a widely-used, general alloy. Even with only a stress relief and no solution treatment, 356 alloy sand castings have a tensile strength of 23,000 PSI and a brinell hardness of 60.

Aluminum-Magnesium Alloys

Alloy #214. 96.2 percent aluminum and 3.8 percent magnesium. This is a straight aluminum-magnesium alloy from which sprung the following variations:

Alloy #A214. 94.4 percent aluminum, 3.8 percent magnesium, and 1.8 percent zinc. By adding the 1.8 percent zinc, the 214 alloy made a very good permanent-mold casting alloy for permold cooking utensils, which is its primary use.

Alloy B214. 94.4 percent aluminum, 3.8 percent magnesium, and 1.8 percent silicon. In this case, the zinc was left out, and 1.8 percent silicon was added. The result was a good alloy for permanent molded cooking utensils and pipe fittings (general and marine use). This change reduced the mechanical properties; however, it improved the foundry properties and corrosion resistance.

Alloy F214. 95.7 percent aluminum, 3.8 percent magnesium, and 0.5 percent silicon. All that changed between alloy B214 and alloy F214 was a reduction by .3 percent in the silicon percentage. This change made the alloy a sand-casting alloy, basically used for sand casting ornamental hardware and architectural castings.

From this you can see that with only minor additions of zinc, magnesium, and silicon in various combinations and percentages, or by simply changing the percentage of any element by a very small amount, you can change the outstanding characteristics in one way or another.

Now let's look back at alloy #214. This alloy is basically used for sand casting food-handling equipment, cooking utensils, chemical and sewage hardware, etc. The tensile strength as-cast is 22,000 PSI, with a brinell hardness of 50.

So, if you jiggle every conceivable alloy around by percentages you can come up with a million different alloys. This, however, is the province of the research metallurgist, who is looking for a superior alloy or one that excels all others, perhaps in only one outstanding characteristic.

Alloy # 220. 90 percent aluminum and 10 percent magnesium. This alloy is heat-treatable with exceptionally high strength and elongation for a sand casting. It requires special foundry practice, especially with gating and risering, because of the high percentage of magnesium. With a T4 heat treatment, the tensile strength is 42,000 PSI with a 12 percent elongation in 2 inches. It will stretch like rubber before breaking. It is not for use where the temperature exceeds 250 degrees Fahrenheit, but is good for castings requiring strength and shock resistance.

Aluminum-Copper-Nickel-Magnesium Alloys

Alloy #142. 92.5 percent aluminum, 4 percent copper, 1.5 percent magnesium, and 2.0 percent nickel. This alloy, because of the 2 percent nickel, is a good alloy for casting parts that must have good strength at elevated temperatures, such as aircraft engine parts, pistons, and cylinder heads. It can be cast in sand or permanent molds. Heat-treated, permanent-mold castings can have a tensile strength of 40,000 PSI or more and a brinell hardness of 110 or more. If sand cast and heat-treated, you can come up with a tensile of 20,000 PSI and a hardness of 85. You will find a good number of aluminum alloys that carry a percentage of nickel.

CHEMICAL CONTROL LIMITS

On the alloys I have just covered, the analysis given is taken as an average. All ingots, regardless of the composition, are produced within a given tolerance. Let's look at three different specifications and limits.

Alloy "A" has copper from 1.0 to 1.5 percent; iron with a maximum of 0.6 percent; silicon from 4.5 to 5.5 percent; magnesium from 0.4 to 0.6 percent; manganese with a 0.1 percent maximum; zinc with a 0.3 percent maximum; titanium 0.2 percent; and aluminum for the remaining percent.

Alloy "B" has copper at 0.2 percent maximum; iron at 0.6 percent maximum; silicon from 6.5 to 7.5 percent; magnesium from 0.2 to 0.4 percent; zinc at 0.3 percent maximum; and aluminum for the remainder.

Alloy "C" has copper from 1.2 to 1.8 percent; iron at a maximum of 0.6 percent; silicon from 4.5 to 5.5 percent; magnesium from 0.4 to 0.6 percent; manganese from 0.5 to 1.0 percent; zinc at a maximum of 0.1 percent; nickel from 0.5 to 1.0 percent; and aluminum as the remainder.

A, B, and C represent the chemical control limits for three different aluminum-silicon heat-treatable alloys. On the face of it, there appears to be little difference in the three alloys. The percentage changes are small; however, there is definite differences in the physical properties of each. The tensile strength, yield strength, and hardness of aluminum-silicon alloys increase with the copper and magnesium content. The addition of these elements much beyond the limits given results in excessive brittleness, however.

To produce an alloy twice as hard as pure aluminum, it would take 15 percent zinc, 8 percent copper, or 4 percent magnesium. The hardening effect of magnesium is therefore twice that of copper and nearly four times that of zinc. The addition of as little as 0.5 percent of magnesium increase the strength of aluminum alloys by 17 percent and the hardness of 10 percent.

Appendix A
Shrinkage Allowances
for Sand-Cast Metals

Typical pattern-makers' shrinkage allowances per foot, for sand casting various metals:

Aluminum Alloys:
　　Small castings of simple design—5/32″
　　Larger castings or those of intricate design—1/8″ to 1/12″.

Brass Alloys—3/16″

Bronze Alloys—3/16″

Gray Iron Alloys—1/10″

Magnesium Alloys—5/32″

Steel Alloys—1/4″

Appendix B

Metalcasting Information

Circular

60 seconds	1 minute
90 degrees	1 quadrant
60 minutes	1 degree
4 quadrants or 360 degrees	1 circle
30 degrees	1 sign

Units of Measure

Acre = 208.71 feet square = 43,560 square feet = 4,480 square yards = 0.40687.
Hectares = 4,046,87 square meters.
Barrel = 196 pounds (Flour = 42 Gal. Oil (Standard Oil Co.).
Board Foot = 1 square foot, 1 inch thick.
Bushel = 4 pecks = 32 quarts = 2,150.42 cubic inches = 1.24446 cubic feet = 35.23928 liters.
Cable (Cable length) = 720 feet = 120 fathoms = 219.457 meters.
Chain = 100 feet = 100 links = 30.48 meters.
Dram (apothecary) = 3 scruples = 60 grams = 3.888 grams.
Fathom = 6 feet = 1.829 meters.
Foot = 12 inches.
Furlong = 660 feet = 40 rods, perches, or poles = ⅛ mile = 201.17 meters.
Gallon = 231 cubic inches = 3.78543 liters = 3,785.43 cubic centimeters.
Gill = ¼ pint.
Grain = 0.0648 grams = 64.8 milligrams.
Hogshead = 63 gallons = 2 barrels (31.5 gallons capacity) = 238.48 liters.
Inch = 2.54 centimeters = 25.4 millimeters.
Karat = 200 milligrams = 0.2 grams = 3.0865 grains.

203

Kilogram = 1,000 grams = 2.20462 pounds avd.

Kilometer = 1,000 meters = 3,280.83 feet = 0.62137 miles.

Knot (Nautical or geographical miles) = 6,080.2 feet = 1.15155 miles = 1.85325 kilometers = 1 minute of earth's circumference.

League = 15,840 feet = 3 miles = 4.828 kilometers.

Link = one hundredth of measuring chain = 12 inches (Engineer's chain) = 7.92 inches (Surveyor's chain) = 20 centimeters (Metric Chain).

Liter = 1,000 cubic centimeters = 61.023 cubic inches = 0.0353 cubic feet = 2.1134 liquid pints = 0.2642 gallons.

Meter = 39.37 inches = 3.28 feet.

Miles = 5,280 feet = 1,760 yards. A square mile equals 640 acres = 2.59 square kilometers.

Milligram = 0.001 grams = 0.015432 grains.

Millimeter = 0.001 meters = 0.03937 inches.

Ounce, Apothecary. Same as troy ounce = 480 grains = 31.104 grams. Avoirdupois = 437.5 grains = 28.35 grams = 0.9115 ounce troy or apothecary. Troy (for gold and silver) = 480 grains = 20 pennyweight = 31.104 grams = 1.097 ounces avd.

Peck = 0.25 bushels = 8.81 liters.

Pennyweight = 24 grains = 1.555 grams.

Pint, liquid = 0.125 gallons = 0.4732 liters. Dry = 0.5 quarts = 0.5506 liters.

Pipe or Butt = 126 gallons = 2 hogsheads = 476.96 liters.

Pounds, Avoirdupois = 7,000 grains = 16 ounces (avd.) = 0.4536 kilograms.

Troy or Apothecary = 5,760 grains = 12 ounces = 0.3732 kilograms.

Quart, liquid = 0.25 gallons = 0.94634 liters. Dry = 0.03125 bushels = 67.2 cubic inches = 1.1 liters.

Rod or Perch or Pole = 16.5 feet = 5.5 yards = 5.0292 meters.

Rood = 0.25 acres = 40 square rods = 1,210 square yards = 1,011.72 square meters.

Scruple = 20 grains = 1.296 grams.

Section of land = 1 mile square = 640 acres.

Stone = 14 pounds (avd.) = 6.35 kilograms.

Ton (gross) Displacement of water = 35.88 cubic feet = 1,016 cubic meters. (gross or long) = 2,240 pounds (avd.) = 1.12 short or net tons = 1,016.05 kilograms = 1.01605 metric tons (net or short) = 2,000 pounds (avd.) = 20 hundred-weight = 907.185 kilograms = 0.907185 metric tons = 0.892857 long tons (metric) = 2,204.62 pounds (avd.) = 1.10231 net tons = 0.9842 long tons = 1,000 kilograms.

Cubic Yard = 27 cubic feet = 46,656 cubic inches = 0.76456 cubic meters. Square yard = 9 square feet = 1,296 square inches = 0.836 square meters. Yard = 3 feet = 36 inches = 0.9144 meters.

CONVERSION TABLES

Volume

Multiply		By	To Obtain
Cubic Centimeters			
Dry Volume	(cm.^{3} or cu.cm.)	0.061023	Cubic Inches
Liquid Volume	(c.c.)	.001000	Liters
Liquid Volume	(c.c.)	0.033814	U.S. Fluid Ounces
Cubic Meters	(m.^{3} or cu. m.)	264.17	Gallons
Cubic Meters	(m.^{3} or cu. m.)	61,023	Cubic Inches

Multiply		By	To Obtain
Cubic Meters	(m.^{3} or cu. m.)	35.315	Cubic Feet
Cubic Meters	(m.^{3} or cu. m.)	1.3079	Cubic Yards
Cubic Feet	(ft^3 or cu. ft.)	1,728.	Cubic Inches
Cubic Feet	(ft.^{3} or cu. ft.)	28,317.	Cubic Centimeters
Cubic Feet	(ft.^{3} or cu. ft.)	0.028317	Cubic Meters
Cubic Feet	(ft.^{3} or cu. ft.)	28.32	Liters
Cubic Feet	(ft.^{3} or cu. ft.)	0.037037	Cubic Yards
Cubic Feet	(ft.^{3} or cu. ft.)	7.4805	U.S. Gallons
Cubic Yards	(ft.^{3} or cu. ft.)	27.	Cubic Feet
Cubic Yards	(yd.^{3} or cu. yds.)	0.76456	Cubic Meters
Liters	(yd.^{3} or cu. yds.)	61.02	Cubic inches
Liters		0.03531	Cubic Feet

Mass and Weight

Multiply	By	To Obtain
Grams (g.)	0.035274	Ounces Avoirdupois
Grams (g.)	0.0022046	Pounds Avoirdupois
Kilograms (kg.)	2.2046	Pounds Avoirdupois
Ounces Avoirdupois (oz.av.)	28.350	Grams
Ounces Apothecary or Troy (oz.ap. or t.)	31.103	Grams
Pounds Avoirdupois (lb.av.)	16.	Ounces Avoirdupois
Pounds Avoirdupois (lb.av.)	453.59	Grams
Pounds Avoirdupois (lb.av.)	0.45359	Kilograms
Pounds Apothecary or Troy (lb.ap. or t.)	12.	Ounces Apothecary or troy
Pounds Apothecary or Troy (lb.ap. or t.)	373.24	Grams
Metric Tons (t)	1,000	Kilograms
Metric Tons (t)	2,204.6	Pounds Avoirdupois
Metric Tons (t)	1.1023	Short Tons
Short Tons	2,000.	Pounds Avoirdupois
Short Tons	907.18	Kilograms
Long Tons	2,240.	Pounds Avoirdupois
Long Tons	1,016.0	Kilograms
Assay Tons	29.167	Grams

Pressure

Multiply	By	To Obtain
Kilograms per Square Centimeter	14.22	Pounds per Square Inch
Kilograms per Square Centimeter	1.024	Short Tons per Square Foot
Kilograms per Square Centimeter	0.9678	Atmospheres
Pounds per Square Inch	0.07031	Kilograms per Square Centimeter
Pounds per Square Inch	0.0720	Short Tons per Square Foot
Pounds per Square Inch	0.06804	Atmospheres
Pounds per Square Inch	2.307	Feet of Water at 39.2°F.
Pounds per Square Inch	2.036	Inches of Mercury at 0°C
Pounds per Square Foot	0.4882	Grams per Square Centimeter
Pounds per Square Foot	0.00050	Short Tons per Square Foot

Length

Multiply		By	To Obtain
Millimeters	(mm.)	0.001	Meters
Millimeters	(mm.)	0.039370	Inches
Centimeters	(cm.)	0.01	Meters
Centimeters	(cm.)	0.39370	Inches
Decimeters	(dm.)	0.1	Meters
Decimeters	(dm.)	3.9370	Inches
Meters	(m.)	39.370	Inches
Meters	(m.)	3.2808	Feet
Kilometers	(km.)	1,000.	Meters
Kilometers	(km.)	3,280.8	Feet
Inches	(in.)	25.400	Millimeters
Inches	(in.)	2.5400	Centimeters
Feet	(ft.)	12.	Inches
Feet	(ft.)	30.480	Centimeters
Feet	(ft.)	0.30480	Meters
Yards	(yd.)	91.440	Centimeters
Yards	(yd.)	0.91440	Meters
Statute Miles (st. mi.)		5,280.	Feet
Statute Miles (st. mi.)		1,760	Yards

Domestic Weights and Measures

Avoirdupois Weight

437½ grains	1 ounce
16 ounces	1 pound
25 pounds	1 quarter
4 quarters	1 cwt.
20 cwt.	1 ton
2,240 pounds	1 long ton

Troy Weight

24 grains	1 pennyweight
20 pwt.	1 ounce
12 ounces	1 pound

Apothecaries' Weight

20 grains	1 scruple
3 scruples	1 dram
8 drams	1 ounce
12 ounces	1 pound

Dry Measure

2 pints
8 quarts
4 pecks
36 bushels

Liquid Measure

4 gills	1 pint
2 pints	1 quart
4 quarts	1 gallon
31½ gallons	1 barrel
2 barrels	1 hogshead

Linear Measure

12 inches	1 foot
3 feet	1 yard
5½ yards-16½ feet	1 rod
320 rods-5280 feet	1 statute mile
6080.20 feet	1 nautical mile

Cubic or Solid Measure

1728 cu. inches	1 cu. foot
27 cu. feet	1 cu. yard
128 cu. feet	1 cord
40 cu. feet	1 ton of ship cargo

Metric Weights and Measures

Metric weights and measures form a decimal system based upon the meter. For convenience, the liter is used as the unit of capacity and the gram as the unit of weight.

The liter equals 1 cubic decimeter

The gram is the weight of 1 cubic centimeter of water at its greatest density.

Parts and multiples of the unit are indicated by the following prefixes.

Milli	(m) meaning	1/1000
Centi	(c) meaning	1/100
Deci	(d) meaning	1/10
Deka	(dk) meaning	10
Hecto	(H) meaning	100
Kilo	(K) meaning	1,000
Myria		10,000

Surface Measure

144 sq. inches	1 sq. ft.
9 sq. feet	1 sq. yard
30¼ sq. yds.	1 sq. rod
160 sq. rods	1 acre
640 acres	1 sq. mile
1 acre	43,560 sq. ft

Comparisons

U. S. bushel	2150.42 cu. inches
Br. Imp bushel	2218.2 cu. inches
U. S. gallon	231 cu. inches
7.481 U. S. gallons	1 cu. foot
6.229 Br. Imp. gallons	1 cu. foot
6 U. S. gallons	5 Br. Imp. gallons
1 cord	about 103 bushels
1 meter	39.37 in (U. S. statute)
1 liter	61.022 cu. in. (U. S. Statute)
1 gram	15.42 grains (U. S. Statute)
25.4 mm.	1 inch
30.48 cm.	1 foot
1 meter	3.281 feet
1.6093 kilometer	1 mile
6.4515 sq. cm.	1 sq. inch
1 sq. meter	10.764 sq. ft.

Comparisons

1 sq. meter	1.550 sq. inches
1 cu. meter	264.4 U. S. gallons
1 kilogram	2.2046 pounds
1,000 kilograms	1 metric ton
1 kg. per sq. cm.	14.223 lbs. per sq. inch

207

Area

Multiply		By	To Obtain
Square Millimeters	(mm.^{2} or sq. mm.)	0.0015500	Square Inches
Square Centimeters	(cm.^{2} or sq. cm.)	0.15500	Square Inches
Square Meters	(m^2 or sq. m.)	1,000.	Square Centimeters
Square Meters	(m.^{2} or sq. m.)	10.764	Square Feet
Square Inch	(in.^{2} or sq. in.)	645.16	Square Millimeters
Square Inch	(in.^{2} or sq. in.)	6.4516	Square Centimeters
Square Feet	(ft.^{2} or sq. ft.)	144.	Square Inches
Square Feet	(ft.^{2} or sq. ft.)	929.03	Square Centimeters
Square Feet	(ft.^{2} or sq.ft.)	0.092903	Square Meters
Square Yards	(yd.^{2} or sq. yd.)	0.83613	Square Meters
Acres	(A)	43,560.	Square Feet
Acres	(A)	4,840.	Square Yards
Acres	(A)	4,046.9	Square Meters
Square Miles	(mi.^{2} or sq. mi.)	640.	Acres

SHRINKAGE OF CASTINGS PER FOOT

Metals	Fractions of an Inch	Decimals of an Inch
Pure Aluminum	13/64	0.2031
Iron, Small Cylinders	1/16	0.0625
Iron, Pipes	1/8	0.1150
Iron, Girders, Beams, etc.	1/64	0.1000
Iron, Large Cylinders, Contraction of Diameter at Top	5/8	0.6250
Iron, Large Cylinders, Contraction of Diameter at Bottom	5/64	0.0830
Iron, Large Cylinders, Contraction in Length	3/32	0.0940
Cast Iron	1/8	0.1250
Steel	1/4	0.2500
Malleable Iron	1/8	0.1250
Tin	1/12	0.0833
Britannia	1/32	0.03125
Thin Brass Castings	11/64	0.1670
Thick Brass Castings	5/32	0.1500
Zinc	5/16	0.3125
Lead	5/16	0.3125
Copper	3/16	0.1875
Bismuth	5/32	0.1563

ESTIMATED WEIGHT OF GRAY IRON CASTINGS FROM PATTERN

Material of Pattern	Multiply Weight of Pattern by	Sp. Gr. of Material
Cedar	17.5	0.40
Red Wood	17.0	0.42

Material of Pattern	Multiply Weight of Pattern by	Sp. Gr. of Material
Poplar	15.8	0.45
Cypress	14.8	0.48
White Pine	14.2	0.50
Birch	13.0	0.55
Yellow Pine	11.6	0.61
Ash	11.1	0.64
Cherry	11.0	0.65
Chestnut	10.9	0.66
Maple	10.4	0.68
Black Walnut	10.0	0.70
Elm	10.0	0.72
Beech	10.0	0.72
Red Oak	9.6	0.74
White Oak	9.2	0.78
Hard Mahogany	8.3	0.85
Hard Rubber	7.3	0.97
Red Fiber	5.1	1.40
Plaster of Paris	3.1	2.27
Aluminum (cast)	2.60	2.80
Zinc	1.00	7.10
Tin	0.97	7.29
Brass (yellow)	0.85	8.37
Copper	0.83	8.50
Bronze (gun metal)	0.82	8.67
Lead	0.63	11.35

MELTING POINT, WEIGHT PER CUBIC FOOT, WEIGHT PER CUBIC INCH, TENSILE STRENGTH, AND SPECIFIC GRAVITY OF METALS

Name	Melting Point Degrees F	Weight Cu. Ft. in Lbs.	Weight Cu. In. in Lbs.		Tensile Strength Per Square Inch in Lbs.	Spec. Grav.
Aluminum	1220	168½	.0975		23,000	2.700
Alum. Bronze (10 percent)	1922	474	.2740		80,000	7.600
Ajax Metal	1850	524	.3030	Cast	38,000	
				Wire	96,000	8.400
Antimony	1167	417	.2415		1,000	6.684
Brass, Common	1725	524	.3030	Cast	20,000	
				Wire	49,000	8.400
Bronze	1920	549	.3178	Cast	32,000	
				Wire	65,000	8.800
Bismuth	520	611½	.3540	Cast	3,200	9.800
Cadmium	610	540	.3125			8.648
Chromium	2940	443	.2560			7,100

Name	Melting Point Degrees F	Weight Cu. Ft. in Lbs.	Weight Cu. In. in Lbs.		Tensile Strength Per Square Inch in Lbs.	Spec. Grav.
Cobalt	2695	55o	.3220			8,900
Copper	1985	537	.3118	Cast	22,500	8,600
Copper Wire		555	.3213	Wire	60,000	8,890
Crown Bronze	1850	524	.3032	Cast	37,500	
				Wire	90,000	8,400
Glass	1600 to 2300	162	.0938			2,600
Gold	1946	1204	.6970			19,300
Gun Metal (9 copper 1 Tin)	1832	549	.3178	Cast	32,000	
				Wire	90,000	8.800
Iridium	4260	1399	.8100			22,420
Iron Cast (Av.)	2175	455½	.2637		16,000-23,500	
Pig (Av.)	2200 to 3000			1st melt	18,000	
				2nd melt	20,000	
				Plates	52,000	7.300
Iron (Wrought)	2750	480½	.2780	Bar, Best	58,000	
				Wire	95,000	7.700
Iron (Wrought) Welding	2400					
Lead	620	707	.4090	Cast	1,800	
				Pipe	2,100	11.337
Manganese Bronze	1940	549	.3178	Cast	57,000	
				Rolled	105,000	8,800
Mercury	38	845	.4890			13,546
Nickel	2645	556	.3220			8,900
Palladium	2830	759	.4397			12,160
Phosphor Bronze	1830	549	.3178	Cast	38,500	
				Wire	96,000	8.800
Platinum	3200	1333	.7717	Wire	53,000	21.370
Silver	1760	655	.3790			10,500
Steel	2610	489	.2830	Plates	60,000	
				Wire	120,000	7.830
Tin	450	455	.2635	Cast	4,600	
				Wire	7,000	7.290
Titanium	3275	281	.1628			4,500
Tungsten	6100	1176	.6800			18,850
Zinc	785	446	.2580	Cast	2,900	
				Wire	20,000	7,140

210

Weight of Castings Determined From Weight of Patterns

— Will Weigh When Cast In —

A Pattern Weighing One Pound Made of	Cast Iron Pounds	Zinc Pounds	Copper Pounds	Yellow Brass Pounds	Gun Metal Pounds	Aluminum Pounds	Lead Pounds
Mahogany, Nassau	10.7	10.4	12.8	12.2	12.5		
Mahogany, Honduras	12.9	12.7	15.3	14.6	15.0		
Mahogany, Spanish	8.5	8.2	10.1	9.7	9.9		
Pine, red	12.5	12.1	14.9	14.2	14.6		
Pine, white	16.7	16.1	19.8	19.0	19.5	5.0	22.0
Pine, yellow	14.1	13.6	16.7	16.0	16.5		
Oak	9.0	8.6	10.4	10.4	10.9		

WEIGHT OF A SQUARE FOOT OF CAST IRON

Thickness in inches	Weight in pounds
1/4	9.37
3/8	14.06
1/2	18.75
5/8	23.43
3/4	28.12
7/8	32.81
1	37.50
1-1/8	42.18
1-1/4	46.87
1-3/8	51.56
1-1/2	56.25
1-5/8	60.93
1-3/4	65.62
1-7/8	70.31
2	75.00

Appendix C
Suppliers

ALABAMA

Benners, T.H. & Co.   *Foundry raw materials, etc.*
701 S. 37th
Birmingham, AL 35222

CALIFORNIA

Asbury Graphite Inc. of Cal.   *All types of graphite*
2855 Franklin Canyon Rd.
Rodeo, CA 94572

Beaver Cut Rotary File Co.   *Foundry supplies, files, rasps, etc.*
Telegraph Rd. & Woods
Los Angeles, CA 90022

Casting Materials Co. Inc.   *Foundry supplies*
4614 S. Hampton St.
Vernon, CA 90048

Electro-Coatings Inc.   *Mold coats*
1601-05 School St.
Moraga, CA 94556

Huntington Beach Plant, Electro Div.   *Refractories, crucibles,*
  Ferro Corp.   *restrainer cores, etc.*
P.O. Box 471
Huntington Beach, CA 92648

Perfect Plank Co.   *Wood laminate for patterns*
1559 Orobrodam Blvd.
Oroville, CA 95965

CONNECTICUT

Capewell Div. Stanadyne Inc.   *Saw blades, chill nails*
61 Governor St.
Hartford, CT 06102

Composition Material Inc.   *Wood flour, fibers, etc.*
26 Sixth St., Dept. TR
Stamford, CT 06905

Neilson, John R. & Sons Inc.   *Wood flour of all types*
252 Chapel Road
South Windsor, CT 06074

FLORIDA

Equipment Co. of America   *Magnesium bottom*
1077 Hialeah Drive   *boards*
Hialeah, FL 33010

GEORGIA

Walker Peenimpac Div.   *Shot and grit*
of Walker Pump Co.
2010 E. Hill Ave. Box 755
Valdosta, GA 31601

ILLINOIS

Acme Resin Co.   *Resins and binders*
1401 Circle Ave.
Forest Park, IL 60130

American Colloid Co.   *Pure Wyoming bentonite*
5100 Suffield Court, Dept. TB
Skokie, IL 60076

Atlantic Chemical &   *Chemical fluxes*
Metals Co.
1925 N. Kenmore Avenue
Chicago, IL 60614

Barco Chemical Products Co.   *Aerosol silicone*
703 S. La Salle St.   *mold release*
Chicago, IL 60605

Black Products Co.
13515 S. Calumet Avenue
Chicago, IL 60627

Foundry core compounds,
facings

Coeval Inc.
St. Joseph, IL 61873

Corncob flour

Gallagher Corp.
3966 Morrison Avenue
Gurnee, IL 60031

Foundry plastics

Ipsen Ceramics
330 John Street
Pecatonica, IL 61063

High-temperature
crucibles, etc.

Midwest Foundry Supply Co.
Edwardsville, IL 62025

Moulder's Friend Inc.
Thomas St.
Dallas City, IL 62330

Foundry sand
conditioners and aerators

Short, J.R. Milling Co.
233 S. Wacker Drive
Chicago, IL 60606

Foundry equipment

Solomon Grinding Service
P.O. Box 1766
Springfield, IL 62705

Iron oxide

Superior Graphite Co.
20 N. Wacker Drive
Chicago, IL 60606

Graphite

INDIANA

Indiana Products Co.
La Salle West Bldg.
South Bend, IN 46601

Foundry facing
and supplies

Pitner & Hess Inc.
Bedford, IN 47421

Organic nonmineral
foundry parting

IOWA

Carver Foundry Products Inc.
Capital Road, Progress Park
P.O. Box 817
Muscatine, IA 52761

Supplies and
machinery

214

KANSAS

Hartman, M.W. Mfg. Co.
400 W. Second
Hutchinson, KS 67501

*Foundry machinery
and equipment*

MARYLAND

Eastern Wood Fibers Inc.
8245 Dorsey Run Road
Jessup, MD 20794

Wood flour, etc.

**Foundry Rubber Inc.,
Para Products Div.**
7841 Airpark Road
Gaithersburg, MD 20760

*Core binders, liquid
partings, etc.*

MASSACHUSETTS

Boston Pattern Works Inc.
595 Pleasant
Norwood, MA 02082

*Castings and
pattern equipment*

**Bullard Abrasive
Products Inc.**
40 Donald Street
Westboro, MA 01581

*Grinding and cutoff
wheels*

Devcon Corp.
59 Endicott Street
Danvers, MA 01923

Plastic steel

MICHIGAN

Acheson Colloids Co.
1637 Washington Street
Port Huron, MI 48060

*Refractory and
colloidal graphite*

Acme Abrasive Co.
24202 Marmon Avenue
Warren, MI 48089

Grinding wheels, etc.

**C.E. Cast Industrial Products
Combuotion Eng. Inc.**
14365 Wyoming Avenue
Detroit, MI 48238

*Refractories and
refractory material*

Chem Trend Inc. Dept. T
3205 E. Grand River
Howell, MI 48843

Mold releases

215

Colloidal Paint Products Co. 6136 Charles Street Detroit, MI 48212	*Graphoidal coatings for metal mold*
Durez-Stevens Foundry Supply 810 Rosewood Ferndale, MI 48220	*Core wash, paste, plumbago, parting, etc.*
Foundries Materials Co. 5 Preston Street Coldwater, MI 49036	*Foundry supplies*
Grav-I-Flo Corp. Norwood and Davidson Sturgis, MI 49091	*Deburring equipment*
Mecha-Finish Corp. Box 308-T Sturgis, MI 49091	*Automatic deburring equipment*
Roto-Finish Co. 3707 Milham Road Kalamazoo, MI 49003	*Finishing and deburring machines, abrasive media*
Severance Tool Industries Inc. 3790 Orange Street P.O. Box 1866-P Saginaw, MI 48605	*Ground high speed and carbide midget mills for removing fins, etc.*
Simpson Russ Co. 21908 Schoenherr Road Warren, MI 48089	*Pattern supplies*
Smillie, C.M. & Co. 1180 Woodward Heights Blvd. Ferndale, MI 48220	*Foundry and plastic supplies*
Spurgeon Co. 1330 Hilton Road Ferndale, MI 48000	*Conveyors, etc.*
Wickes Engineered Materials Div. 1621 Holland Avenue Saginaw, MI 48601	*Sand conditioner and ingot mold wash*

216

MINNESOTA

Sterling Machine &
Supply Co.
2222 Elm S. E.
Minneapolis, MN 55414

Foundry supplies

Technical Ceramics
Products Div.
3M Center
St. Paul, MN 55101

Strainer cores

MISSOURI

Products Engineering Co.
Cape Girardeau, MO 63701

Foundry jackets
and liners

NEW JERSEY

Asbury Graphite Mills
Inc.
41 Main Street
Asbury, NJ 08802

Foundry facings,
blackings, and plumbago

Certech Inc.
53-57 Bergentine Avenue
Westwood, NJ 07675

Injection molded ceramics

Lignum Chemical Works
No. 5-foot of Jersey Avenue
Jersey City, NJ 07302

Sawdust, wood flour

Springfield Facing
Corp.
401 S. 2nd Street
Harrison, NJ 07029

Foundry facings
and supplies

Whitehead Brothers Co.
66 Hanover Road
Florham Park, NJ 07932

Foundry sand and
supplies

NEW YORK

Belmont Metals Inc.,
Div. of Belmont Metal
& Refining Wks.
320 Belmont Avenue
Brooklyn, NY 11207

Smelters and refiners
of all nonferrous
metals

Exolon Company (The)
950 E. Niagara Street
Tonawanda, NY 14150

*Aluminum oxide and
silicon carbide
abrasive, etc.*

**Ferro Corp. Electro
Div.**
661 Willet Road
Buffalo, NY 14218

*Refractory strainer cores,
riser tile, runner, gate
tile, and breaker cores*

Great Lakes Carbon Corp.
Graphite Products Div.
229 Park Avenue
New York, NY 10017

*Graphite powders,
chill rods, fluxing
tubes, etc.*

**Liberty Steel
& Metals Corp.**
Time & Life Bldg.
Rockefeller Center
New York, NY 10020

*Copper shot, master
alloys, ferro alloys*

**NL Industries Inc.,
Tam Div.**
Box C, Bridge Station
Niagara Falls, NY 14305

*Zirconium oxides,
silicates and chemicals*

**Pancoast International
Corp.**
3-5 Park Row
New York, NY 10038

*Copper shot, master
alloys, ferro alloys*

Polymer Applications Inc.
3443 River Road
Tonawanda, NY 14150

*Shell mold and
cold set resins*

Precise Alloys Inc.
69-T Kinkel Street
Westbury, NY 11590

*Solders, lead,
lead casting, etc.*

Remet Corp.
Dept. A P.O. Box 278
278 Bleachery Place
Chadwicks, NY 13319

*Foundry facings and
supplies*

**Sirotta Bernard Co
Inc.**
65-35th Street
Brooklyn, NY 11232

*Nut shell blast
cleaning abrasives, etc.*

Unicast Development Corp.
345 Tompkins Avenue
Pleasantville, NY 10570

*Cer. and high
temperature facings core
and mold binders*

218

United Compound Co. 611 Indian Church Road Buffalo, NY 14224	*Vent wax*

OHIO

Akron Porcelain Co. P.O. Box 3767 Akron, OH 44310	*Foundry strainer cores*
Andersons Cob **Division (The)** 519 Illinois Avenue Mansfield, OH 44901	*Steel and iron* *shot and grit* *for blast cleaning*
Ashland Chemical Co. P.O. Box 2219 Columbus, OH 43216	*Binders, seacoal,* *core and mold* *washers, etc.*
Barium & Chemicals **Inc.** Steubenville, OH 44870	*Foundry chemicals*
BMM Inc. 7777 Wall Street Cleveland, OH 44125	*Foundry equipment*
Borden Chemical Div. **of Borden Inc.** 180-T E. Broad Street Columbus, OH 43215	*Binders, adhesives,* *resins, etc.*
Brown Insulating **Systems Inc.** 11943 Abbey Road North Royalton, OH 44133	*Insulating riser* *shapes, etc.*
Buckeye Products Co. 7021 Vine Street Cincinnati, OH 45216	*Foundry supplies* *and equipment*
C.E. Cast **Industrial Products** 4401 Creekside Avenue Toledo, OH 43612	*Permanent mold coatings,* *partings, sealants, etc.*
C.E. Cast Industrial **Products Arcoa Div.** 4401 Creekside Avenue Toledo, OH 43612	*Refractory core,* *mold coatings, and* *binders.*

Cedar Heights Clay Co.
P.O. Box 295
Oak Hill, OH 45656

Yellow bonding clay

**Cleveland Metal
Abrasive Inc.**
305 Euclid Office Plaza
Cleveland, OH 44101

*Abrasives for blast
cleaning castings,
etc.*

**Diamonite Products
Div. of Spartex**
P.O. Box TR
Shreve, OH 44676

*Aluminum oxide
ceramic products,
sandblast nozzles*

Exomet, Inc.
Box 647-T
Conneaut, OH 44030

*Insulating products,
core and mold castings*

Foseco Inc.
P.O. Box 81227
Cleveland, OH 44181

*Foundry coatings and
flux, etc.*

Freeman Mfg. Co.
1150 E. Broadway
Toledo, OH 43604

*Pattern shop and
foundry supplies
and equipment*

Globe Steel Abrasive Co.
Laird & First Avenue
Mansfield, OH 44901

*Steel and iron
shot and grit for
blast cleaning*

Hill & Griffith Co.
1265-1267 State Avenue
Cincinnati, OH 45204

*Foundry facings and
supplies*

**Inland Refractories
Co.**
10235 Berea Road
Cleveland, OH 44102

*Cupola gun mix,
brick, clay, etc.*

Kindt-Collins Co.
12655 Elmwood Avenue
Cleveland, OH 44111

*Rapping plates, pattern
supplies, wax
products, etc.*

**Louthan Plant
Div. Ferro Corp.**
P.O. Box 781
East Liverpool, OH 43920

*Gating and risering
tile, strainer cores,
refractory specialties, etc.*

Metal Blast Inc. 871 E. 67th Street Cleveland, OH 44103	*Iron and steel shot and grit*
Nordson Corp. 314 Jackson Street Amherst, OH 44001	*Hot paste applicators*
Ransom & Randolph Co. Chestnut & Superior Sts. Toledo, OH 43604	*Investments*
Rudow Mfg. Co. Sandusky, OH 44870	*Shell sand runner tubes and pouring basins*
Smith Facing & Supply Co. 1859 Carter Road Cleveland, OH 44113	*Grinders of seacoal, etc.*
Tyler, W.S. Inc., C.E. Equipment Div. 7887-T Hub Pkwy. Cleveland, OH 44125	*Mold washes, core binders, sand, mold coatings, etc.*
Universal Clay Products Co. 1500 First Street Sandusky, OH 44870	*Refractory gating components*

PENNSYLVANIA

Abrasive Metals Co. 2602 Smallman Street Pittsburgh, PA 15222	*Chilled and malleable shot and grit, etc.*
Allegheny Enterprises Industrial Park Zelienople, PA 16063	*Metallurgical chemicals, foundry supplies*
Du-Co Ceramics Co. Mill Run Road Saxonburg, PA 16056	*Ceramic insulation, high-temperature refractories, etc.*
Durasteel Abrasive 2602 Smallman Street Pittsburgh, PA 15222	*Electric arc furnace cast steel shot and grit*

221

Foundry Warehousing & Supply Co. A.V.R.R. & 33rd Street Pittsburgh, PA 15201	*Facings and supplies*
Fuel Equipment Co. 104 Fourth Street Pittsburgh, PA 15215	*Heaters, dryers, gas burners*
Grafos Colloids Corp. 299 Wilkes Place Sharon, PA 16146	*Manufacturers colloidal graphite lubricants, etc.*
Limewood Corp. R.D. 1 Boyers, PA 16020	*Foundry facings*
McGee Industries Inc. 9 Crozerville Road Aston, PA 19014	*Fluorocarbon mold release compound*
Pennsylvania Foundry Supply and Sand Co. 6801 State Road Bldg. B Philadelphia, PA 19135	
Pettinos, George F. Inc. 123 Coulter Avenue Ardmore, PA 19003	*Sands and gravel, refractory cements, graphites, etc.*
Pittsburgh Metals & Purifying Div. P.O. Box 260 Saxonburg, PA 16056	*Exothermic and insulating compounds*
Saxonburg Ceramics Inc. 100 Isabelle Street Saxonburg, PA 16056	*Refractories, strainer cores, crucibles, etc.*
Shamokin Filler Co. Shamokin, PA 17872	*Carbon fillers and additives*
United Erie Inc. 1429 Walnut Street Erie, PA 16512	*Resins, core oils, grease, etc.*
Wallace, M.E. Co. Carbon Street Sunbury, PA 17801	*Carbon compounds*

222

Watsontown Products Co. Watsontown, PA 17777	*Fillers, foundry* *facings, etc.*

TENNESSEE

Porter Warner **Industries Inc.** 3819 Dorris Street Chattanooga, TN 37410	*Molding sands, glass* *sands, clays, talcs*

TEXAS

ACF Plant Electro **Div. Ferro Corp.** E. Duncan Street Tyler, TX 75701	*Gating and risering* *tile, strainer cores*

NL Industries **Baroid Division** P.O. Box 1675 Houston, TX 77001	*P-1 oil catalyst* *and hinge tubes*

VERMONT

Vermont Talc Inc. 46 Mill Street Chester, VT 05143	*Talc and soapstone* *facings*

VIRGINIA

Blue Ridge Talc Inc. Henry, VA 24102	*Talc and soapstone* *facings*

WASHINGTON

Northwest Olivine 5515 Fourth Avenue, S. Seattle, WA 98134	*Olivine*

Technical Specialties **International** 487 Elliott Avenue, W. Seattle, WA 08110	*Precision casting* *waxes, injection mold* *waxes*

WISCONSIN

Ace Mfg. Co. Mary & Wisconsin Streets Weyauwega, WI 54983	*Slotted brass and* *aluminum core* *box vents, etc.*

Donald Sales &	*Seacoal, pitch,*
Mfg. Co.	*core comp.*
6601 W. State	
Milwaukee, WI 53213	

Merit Corp. — *Foundry facings and supplies*
2400 S. 43rd
Milwaukee, WI 53219

Milwaukee Chaplet & — *Chaplets and chills*
Mfg. Co. Inc.
17000 W. Rogers Drive
New Berline, WI 53151

Solvox Mfg. Co. — *Metal Cleaners, foundry fluxes*
11727 W. Fairview Avenue
Milwaukee, WI 53226

Thiem Corp. — *Foundry facings and compounds*
9800 W. Rogers
Milwaukee, WI 53227

FOUNDRY PLANT EQUIPMENT

CONNECTICUT

Bradford Vibrator Co., — *Pneumatic and electric operated foundry vibrators*
Div. of Electro
Mechanics Inc.
152 John Downey Drive
New Britain, CT 06051

FLORIDA

QC Inc. — *New and used blast cleaning equipment*
1450 Southwest 12th Avenue
Pompano Beach, FL 33060

ILLINOIS

Abrading Machinery — *Barrel and vibrating equipment*
& Supply Co.
2336 W. Wabsania Avenue
Chicago, IL 60647

Beardsley & Piper Div. — *Sandslingers, sand conditioning and molding equipment*
of Pettibone
5503 W. Grand Avenue
Chicago, IL 60639

224

Kassnel Vibrator Co.
5990 N. River Road
Rosemont, IL 60018

Foundry vibrators

Martin Engineering Co.
Rte. 34 Dept. TR
Neponset, IL 61345

*Foundry
equipment*

Whiting Corporation
15700 Lathrop Avenue
Harvey, IL 60426

*Complete
foundry
equipment*

IOWA

Adams Co. (The)
Philip & Adams Streets
Dubuque, IA 52001

*Flasks, jackets,
bands, bottom
plate, sprue cutters*

Ohler Machinery Co.
100 Industry Avenue
Waterloo, IA 50704

*Small inexpensive
core sand mixer*

MASSACHUSETTS

Tex Specialties Inc.
265 Swanton Street
Winchester, MA 01890

*Coreless induction
furnace, etc.*

MICHIGAN

Keyes-Davis Co.
64 14th Street
Battle Creek, MI 49016

*Aluminum bottom
boards*

Roberts Corp.
P.O. Box 13160T
Lansing, MI 48901

Foundry equipment

MINNESOTA

Crown Iron Works Fdry.
Equip. Div.
P.O. Box 1364
1300 Tyler St. NE
Minneapolis, MN 55440

*Sand mixers,
foundry equipment*

NEW JERSEY

Inductotherm Corp.
12 Indel Avenue
Rancocas, NJ 08073

*Induction melting
and heating equipment*

225

Pyro-Serv Instruments
Locust Avenue & River Road
North Arlington, NJ 07032

Hand pyrometers

Whitehead Brothers Co.
66 Hanover Road
Florham Park, NJ 07932

*Foundry sand
and supplies*

NEW YORK

Alexander Saunders & Co.
Route 301
Cold Spring, NY 10516

*Investment
casting equipment,
foundry
equipment and supplies*

Casting Supply House Inc.
62 West 47th Street
New York, NY 10036

*Nonferrous
investment, wax
foundry supplies*

Chemaperm Magnetics Inc.
230-T Crossways Park Drive
Woodbury, NY 11797

*Magnetic plates,
pulleys and
drums*

Haywood Supply Co. Inc.
540 S. Columbus Avenue
Mt. Vernon, NY 07307

Sand handling

Unicast Development Corp.
345 Tomphins Avenue
Pleasantville, NY 10570

*Casting equip-
ment, foundry,
facings and
supplies*

OHIO

American Monorail
P.O. Box 4338T
Cleveland, OH 44143

*Hot metal delivery
and pour-off systems*

Cleveland Products Inc.
P.O. Drawer 2754T
Cleveland, OH 44111

*Green sand
molding systems,
molding, coremaking
and mold handling equipment*

Jeffrey Mfg. Div.
Dresser Ind.
P.O. Box 2251-T
400 W. Wilson Bridge Rd.
Columbus, OH 43216

*Flask handling,
continuous mullers,
mold conveyors*

Macleod Co. (The)
11125 Mosteller Road
Cincinnati, OH 45241

*Metal scrap washing
and cleaning
machinery*

226

Marketeers Inc.
19101 Villa View Road
Cleveland, OH 44119

*Investment casting
equipment and
supplies*

Rose Metal Industries Inc.
1538 E. 43rd Street
Cleveland, OH 44103

*Skimmers,
tongs, ladles in
stock*

Walsh, Frank A. & Sons Inc.
13004 Athens Avenue
Cleveland, OH 44107

*Sandblast
equipment, tumbling
mills, dust
collecting systems*

Young & Bertke Co.
2213-15 Winchell Avenue
Cincinnati, OH 45214

*Dust and fuel
control systems*

FOUNDRY METALS

CALIFORNIA

Kayser Aluminum
6250 E. Banbini Boulevard
Los Angeles, CA 90016

Aluminum ingots

COLORADO

C.F. & I. Steel Corp.
P.O. Box 1830
Pueblo, CO 81002

Foundry pig iron

ILLINOIS

H. Kramer & Co.
1315 W. 21st Street
Chicago, IL 60608

*Brass, bronze, and alu-
minum ingots, etc.*

Interlake Inc.
135th St. & Perry Ave.
Chicago, IL 60627

Foundry pig iron

NEW YORK

**American Smelting &
Refining Co.**
120 Broadway
New York, NY 10005

*Brass, bronze, alum-
inum ingots, deoxidizers,
phos. copper, lead,
copper, etc. Sales
offices in 15 major U.S.
cities and Canada.*

Belmont Smelting &
Refining Works Inc.
300 Belmont Avenue
Brooklyn, NY 11207

*Brass, bronze, and
aluminum ingots,
deoxidizers, hard-
eners, white metals, etc.*

OHIO

I. Schumann & Co.
22501 Alexander Road
Cleveland, OH 44146

*Brass and bronze
ingots*

Jackson Iron & Steel Co.
Lick Township
Jackson, OH 45640

*Foundry pig
iron*

PENNSYLVANIA

Alcoa
1222 Alco Bldg.
Pittsburgh, PA 15219

Aluminum ingots

National Steel Corp.
2800 Grant Bldg.
Pittsburgh, PA 15219

Foundry pig iron

Sitkin Smelting & Refining Co.
P.O. Box 708
Lewistown, PA 17044

*Brass,
bronze ingots, etc.*

TEXAS

Lone Star Steel Co.
2200 W. Mockingbird Lane
Dallas, TX 75235

Foundry pig iron

VIRGINIA

Reynolds Metals Co.
P.O. Box 27003ZA
Richmond, VA 23261

Aluminum ingots

MOLDING MACHINES

CONNECTICUT

Bradford Vibrator Co.
150 John Downey Drive
New Britain, CT 06051

*Div. Electro
Mechanics*

OHIO

Cleveland Products Inc.
P.O. Box 2754T
Cleveland, OH 44111

228

Osborn Mfg. Co. (The)
5401 Hamilton Avenue
Cleveland, OH 44114

PENNSYLVANIA

Mac Erie Mfg. Co.
1114 Walnut Street
Erie, PA 16512

Tabor Industries Inc.
840 W. Main Street
Lansdale, PA 19446

TEXAS

National Air Vibrator Co.
6880 Wynnwood Lane
Houston, TX 77008

FOUNDRY SANDS

ARKANSAS
Arkhola Sand & Gravel
P.O. Box 1627
Ft. Smith, AR 72901

CALIFORNIA

Del Monte Properties Co.
P.O. Box 567
Pebble Beach, CA 93953

FLORIDA

Edgar Plastic Kaolin Co.
Box 8
Edgar, FL 32049

ILLINOIS

Bell Rose Silica Co.
Central Life Bldg. at Ruby
Ottawa, IL 61350

INDIANA

Arrowhead Silica Corp.
Box 67
Chestertown, IN 46304

Hardy Sand Co.
Box 629
Evansville, IN 47701

MICHIGAN

Foundries Material Co.
5 Preston St.
Coldwater, MI 49036

Great Lakes Minerals Co.
2855 Coolidge Hwy. Suite 202-T
Troy, MI 48084

Sargent Sand Co.
2844 Bay Road
Saginaw, MI 48603

OHIO

Inland Refractories Co.
10235 Berea Rd.
Cleveland, OH 44102

PENNSYLVANIA

Penn Foundry Supply & Sand Co.
6801 State Rd. Bldg. B
Philadelphia, PA 19135

UTAH

American Gilsonite Co.
1150 Kennecott Bldg.
Salt Lake City, UT 84133

MISCELLANEOUS FOUNDRY SUPPLIES AND EQUIPMENT

CALIFORNIA

Wax Company of America   *Wax*
5016 West Jefferson Blvd.
Los Angeles, CA 90016

COLORADO

Ammen, C.W. and Son   *Bronze furnaces*
966 Manitou Ave.
Manitou Springs, CO 80829

CONNECTICUT

Amax Nickel Inc.   *Nickel*
1 Greenwich Plaza
Greenwich, CT 06831

Stauffer Chemical Co.   *Ethyl silicate*
Specialty Chem. Div.
Westport, CT 06880

Wire Tex Mfg. Co.   *Hand riddles*
Mason & Picree Sts.
Bridgeport, CT 06605

DELAWARE

Dupont Co.   *Foundry sands and*
Room 36357   *chemicals*
Wilmington, DE 19898

IOWA

Adams Co. (The)   *Flasks*
Philip & Adams St.
Dubuque, IA 52001

Sioux Tools Inc.   *Grinders, etc.*
2901 Floyd Blvd.
Sioux City, IA 51102

ILLINOIS

Beardsley & Piper   *Mullers*
2541 N. Keeler Ave.
Chicago, IL 60639

Chicago Latex   *Rubber*
3017 West Montrose Ave.
Chicago, IL 60618

Hunter Automated   *Molding mach.*
Mach. Co.   *automatic*
2222 Hammond Drive
Schamburg, IL 60196

International Minerals   *Sand Olivine*
& Chemicals Foundry Products Div.
666 Garland Place
Des Plaines, IL 60016

International Molding Machine Co.
1201 N. Barnsdale Road
Lagrange Park, IL 60525

MC-Englevan Heat
Treating & Mfg. Co.
Box 31 708-T Griggs St.
Danville, IL 61832

Metal melting
furnaces

National Engineering Co.
20 North Wacker Drive
Chicago, IL 60606

Mullers

Ottawa Silica Co.
Box 577A
Ottawa, IL 61350

Sand

Smith & Richardson
Mfg. Co.
705 May St.
Geneva, IL 60134

Chaplets
and hinge tubes

Wedron Silica
Pebble Beach Corp.
400 West Higgins Road
Park Ridge, IL 60068

INDIANA

Wheelabrator Frye Inc.
505 S. Byrkit
Michawaka, IN 46544

KANSAS
Great Western Mfg. Co.
Leavenworth, KS 66048

Miscellaneous

MASSACHUSETTS

GCA Corp., Vacuum Ind. Division
34 Linden St.
Somerville, MA 02143

MICHIGAN

American Induction
Heating Corp.
5353 Concord Ave.
Detroit, MI 48211

Ind. furnaces

Crescent Chaplets Inc.
5766 Trumbull Ave.
Detroit, MI 48202

Dietert, Harry W. Co.
9330 Rose Lawn
Detroit, MI 48204

*Sand testing
equipment*

**Kerr Manufacturing
Co.**
1111 E. Milwaukee
Detroit, MI 48204

Prepared investments

MINNESOTA

BMM Western Inc.
333 W. 78th
Minneapolis, MN 55420

Molding machines

3M Co.
3M Center
St. Paul, MN 55101

*Abrasives, pattern
supplies*

MISSOURI

American Flask Co.
2745 South West Blvd.
Kansas City, MO 64108

Flasks

Green, A.P. Refractories
Green Blvd.
Mexico, MO 65265

M.A. Bell Co.
217 Lombard
St. Louis, MO 63102

Miscellaneous

**Products Engineering
Co.**
Cape Girardeau, MO 63701

Miscellaneous

Stahl Specialty Co.
Kingsville, MO 64061

Miscellaneous

NEW JERSEY

Brown Dover Corp.
North Brunswick, NJ 08902

Induction melters

Joseph Dixon   *Crucibles*
Div. 48-C
Wayne & Monmouth St.
Jersey City, NJ 07303

NEW YORK

Hanna Furnace Corp.
1299 Union Rd.
Buffalo, NY 14224

International Nickel   *Nickel*
Co. Inc.
New York, NY 10004

Kilns Supply &   *Kilns*
Service Corp.
P.O. Box Q
Mamaroneck, NY 10543

New York Sand   *Albany and French*
and Facing Co.   *sands*
106-114 Grand Avenue
Brooklyn, NY 11232

Reichhold Chemicals Inc.   *Foundry resins*
Foundry Products Group
525 North Broadway
White Plain, NY 10603

Sculpture House   *Sculpter supplies*
38 E. 30th Street
New York, NY 10016

Union Carbide Corp.   *Ferro alloys*
Metals Div.
270 Park Ave.
New York, NY 10017

OHIO

Ajax Magnethermic   *Induction melters*
Corp.
Warren, OH 44482

Black & Decker Air   *Air tools*
Tool Division
6225 Cochran Road
Solon, OH 44139

234

Brown Insulating Systems
11941 Abbey Rd.
Cleveland, OH 44133

Riser sleeves

Cedar Heights Clay Co.
50 Portsmouth Road
Oak Hill, OH 45656

Clay

Cleveland Crane
Wickliffe, OH 44092

Combustion Engineering Inc.
7887 Hub Parkway
Cleveland, OH 44125

Ladles, etc.

EGC Enterprises Inc.
7315 Industrial Parkway
Mentor, OH 44060

Miscellaneous

Fremont Flask Co.
1000 Wolfe Ave.
Fremont, OH 43420

Snap flasks

Fremont Flask Co.
1420 Wolfe Ave.
Fremont, OH 43420

Flasks

Hines Flask Co.
3431 W. 140th St.
Cleveland, OH 44111

Flasks

Midmark Corp.
Minster, OH 45865

Ladles

Murphy, Jas. A. & Co. Inc.
1421 E. High St.
Hamilton, OH 45011

Pistol Sprayer

North American Refractories
900 Hanna Bldg.
East 14th & Euclid
Cleveland, OH 44115

Osborn Mfg. Corp.
5401 Hamilton Ave.
Cleveland, OH 44114

Molding machines

235

Permaflex Mold Co.	*Rubber*
1919 E. Livingston Ave.	
Columbus, OH 43209	
Shalco Systems	*Shell core machine*
12819 Coit Road	
Cleveland, OH 44108	

PENNSYLVANIA

Clearfield Machine Co.	*Rotary furnaces*
Clearfield, PA 16830	
Electro-melt Corp.	*Furnaces*
32nd St. P.O. Box 4023	
Pittsburgh, PA 15201	
Electro-nite	*Miscellaneous*
Caroline Rd.	
Philadelphia, PA 19154	
Fox Grinders Inc.	*Grinders*
Harmony, PA 16037	
Hauck Mfg. Co.	*Miscellaneous*
P.O. Box 90	
Lebanon, PA 17042	
Herman Corp.	*Molding machines*
West New Castle St.	
Zelienople, PA 16063	
Royer Foundry &	*Sand Cond.*
Machine Co.	
159 Pringle St.	
Kingston, PA 18704	
Vesuvious Crucible Co.	
3636 Blvd of the Allies	
Pittsburgh, PA 15213	

WISCONSIN

Modern Equipment Co.	*Cupolas*
Box 266	
Port Washington, WI 53074	

Appendix D
Relative Weights

Relative weights of equal volumes of various metals follow.

Metal	Relative Weight
Magnesium	0.644
Pure Aluminum	1.0
Zinc	2.65
Gray Iron	2.65
Tin	2.71
Cast Steel	2.90
Cast Brass (Yellow Brass)	3.09
Cast Bronze (Tin Bronze)	3.26
Nickel	3.30
Copper	3.31
Lead	4.20

i.e. If an aluminum casting weighed 3 pounds, the same casting in yellow brass would weigh 9.27 pounds.

Weight of casting determined from pattern weight.

For white pine patterns use the following multipliers:

Aluminum, 8; Cast iron, 16.7; Copper, 19.8; Yellow Brass, 19; Steel, 17.

Multiply the weight of the pattern by the multiplier for the desired metal to get the approximate weight of the casting. i.e. a casting made in aluminum from a white pine pattern that weighs 2 pounds will weigh 16 pounds. In cast iron, the casting from the 2-pound pattern would weigh 33.4 pounds.

Appendix E
Approximate
Analysis Various
Grades Scrap Aluminum

Material	Cu	Fe	Zn	Si	Misc
Crankcase	7–8	1–1.25	1–1.5	1–1.5	
Misc Cast	7–8	1–1.25	1–1.5	1–2	
Cable	0–0.10	.2–.50	0–0.2	0.2–0.4	
Pistons	8–9	0.76–1.25	0.1–0.5	0.75–1.25	
New Clips	0.1–0.3	0.3–0.8	0–0.2	0.2–0.7	
Alum Die Cast	6–7	1–1.5	1–2	2–3	Ni 0.5–1.0
Dural Clips	4–4.5	0.5–1.	0–0.25	0.25–0.5	Mg 0.5–1.0
					Mn 0.5–1.5
Pots—Pans					
Dishes	0.25–0.50	0.50–0.60	0.25–0.50	0.25–0.50	

Appendix F
Casting Alloys
of Aluminum Cans

Melted Al Cans	50/50 Al-Si	50/50 Al-Cu	Tensile Strength
90 lbs.	10 lbs.		20,000 PSI
84 lbs.	16 lbs.		19,000 PSI
80 lbs.	4 lbs.	16 lbs.	22,000 PSI
84 lbs.	8 lbs.	8 lbs.	21,000 PSI
80 lbs.	16 lbs.	4 lbs.	22,000 PSI
70 lbs.	18 lbs.	12 lbs.	25,000 PSI
70 lbs.	26 lbs.	4 lbs.	21,000 PSI
56 lbs.	24 lbs.	20 lbs.	26,000 PSI
74 lbs.	26 lbs.		19,000 PSI

50/50 Al-Si = 50% aluminum, 50% silicon master alloy.
50/50 Al-Cu = 50% aluminum, 50% copper master alloy.
The aluminum cans should be melted first and cast into ingots. To make one of these aluminum can alloys, add the master alloys to the crucible, then add the aluminum can pigs next. After the casting is melted and superheated to 1500 degrees Fahrenheit, stir and skim. Allow to cool to pouring temperature, and cast or pig the melt for remelting and casting.

Index

241

Edited by Suzanne L. Cheatle